Published 1978 by
The Hamlyn Publishing Group Limited
London · New York · Sydney · Toronto
Astronaut House, Feltham, Middlesex, England
© Copyright 1978 by the Hamlyn Publishing Group Limited
ISBN 0 600 38264 8

Printed in Great Britain, by Morrison and Gibb.

THE STORIES AND VERSES IN THIS BOOK ARE BY

MARIA ARMITAGE
GRETA COATES
RACHEL CALLON
CHARLES CONNELL
ELIZABETH COOPER
PAMELA DORMER
JOAN EADINGTON
IVY EASTWICK
JUDITH GLOVER
JANICE GODFREY
JENNY HEAPE
TYTUS HUFFMAN
EDNA HUTCHINGS
BERYL JOHNSTON

SAL KEEGAN
JILL KEVAN
VALERIE ANNE LLOYD
SUE MAILLEY
GILLIAN MAXWELL
MABEL McINTOSH
ROSEMARY POLLITT
ANNE ROBERTSON
GORDON SNELL
MARGARET TORRINGTON
JANE WALLER
FREDA WARD
BARBARA WILLIAMS

THE ILLUSTRATIONS ARE BY

DAVID BARNETT
GINNY CHALCRAFT
GWEN GREEN

CAROLINE SHARPE
LESLEY SMITH
JOHN SPEIRS

366 Bedtime Tales

Hamlyn
London · New York · Sydney · Toronto

Contents

Answers

12 Ride on the wind a kite

14 Six hidden parcels behind the cushion; in the tiger's mouth; in the wicker basket; behind the picture; in the plant pot; under the table

16 Mystery of the missing animals an ostrich on the weather vane; an elephant in the rocks; a porcupine in the grass; a giraffe behind the tree; a snake in the tree; a lion in the barn

19 The vet the mouse is hiding behind the dish

29 Bubbles four, four and two

38 Upside down farm the dog should be in the kennel; the horse should be in the stable; the pig should be in the sty; the rabbit should be in the hutch

48 The odd-one-out the caravan furthest to the right has no chimney

59 How many eyes? twelve eyes; twenty eyes; twenty-four eyes

66 It's all very odd a hare (hair); a palm; a carpet; a field of corn; a potato; a shoe

77 The right time Daddy's watch is right

80 What toys are we? a book; a ball; a boat; a cot; a car; a train

97 The mischievous wind the statue; the inn sign; the canoe; the pocket in the man's suit; the windscreen wiper on the car; the chimney

98 Do you know who I am? the church spire; the train; a needle

109 My bag of sweets one sweet

111 Who are we? porcupines

121 Can you guess? a double-decker bus

126 Football match the ball is hidden in the bicycle chain; one football net is flying from the chimney and the other is hidden on the wall; the whistle is on the tree trunk

138 Santa's secret present roller-skates

151 Help the Fairy Queen reach her palace road 4 leads to the palace gates

152 Naughty kittens the ginger kitten has the blue wool; the black kitten has the green wool; the grey kitten has the yellow wool; the tortoise-shell kitten has the red wool

155 Biscuits for tea fifteen biscuits are eaten altogether

173 Counting eggs three eggs are left

179 How many monkeys? eight monkeys

182 Find the rabbits in the trees; on the roof; on the bird-bath; shadow in the grass; in front of the house; in the cloud

186 The missing chicks there are nine chicks to find

188 Guess what I am? a nose

192 Pick a flower a dandelion

195 Legs eleven legs

205 Old Man Glens four hens

208 Bobbing balloons purple

213 Riddle me a river

218 Ducklings in a line three ducklings

226 So many shoes! eight shoes

Inch Elf in Buttercup Wood

In a land far away lived a tiny man whose name was Inch. He was one inch or two and a half centimetres high. Inch was a very tiny little elf.

His house was a waterlily and it was beautiful, but Inch wasn't happy.

All the other elves lived in Buttercup Wood and had toadstool houses but Inch was so tiny that he couldn't reach high enough to paint a toadstool – and all elf houses are painted bright colours.

'If only I could grow,' cried Inch, and he lay back on his waterlily bed, and tried to wish himself taller. It was no good – he was still tiny.

BUMP – suddenly the waterlily stopped and Inch rolled into the water.

'Oh my,' said a deep voice, 'I am sorry. I didn't see you coming.'

'Help me out,' Inch cried, 'before I shrink.'

The stranger pulled Inch up onto the bank.

'Who are you?' asked Inch.

'I am Oliver Otter, and I'm repairing the river bank.'

Inch told Oliver how he longed to live on a toadstool.

'You need a ladder,' said Oliver.

'What is a ladder?' enquired Inch.

'I will make one for you,' Oliver Otter said, and he did.

Inch painted his toadstool in bright colours, and when it was finished he invited Oliver for tea.

Fun at the circus

David was very excited. His mummy had taken him to the circus for a birthday treat. There were horses, acrobats, elephants, and, best of all, a space ship circled high up in the big tent.

The market stall

I know a smart and jaunty stoat,
With batchelor's buttons on his coat,
Who has a market stall.
His foxgloves and his ladies' smocks
Delight each fashion-conscious fox
Who makes a shopping call.

'Fine grannies' bonnets, cobweb shawls,
And ladies' slippers fit for balls,
Are here for all to see.'
And then at six he closes down,
Packs his suitcase, large and brown,
And walks home to his tea.

Then searching through the fields he goes
For Queen Anne's lace to trim the clothes
He'll sell next day in town.

'Oh!' cried David. 'A space ship! I've always wanted to see one.'

Then Bimbo and Binkie the clowns tumbled on. They climbed ladders with buckets of water, throwing it about until they were both soaked. How everyone laughed!

Later Bimbo came round with balloons for the children.

'I hope there's one left for me,' said David. But when Bimbo reached him, every balloon had gone. He made a very funny face and said, 'Why I believe you're going to cry.'

'Of course I'm not,' said David. 'Boys don't cry when they're five years old, and I'm five today.'

'Five today! Well I must do something about that.'

So Bimbo came back with more balloons, and also a lovely picture of the space ship which he gave to David. 'Happy birthday,' he said. 'Come back and see us again next year.'

11

The jumping cow

The cow who jumped over the moon was tired of that game and wanted to jump over something else.

She jumped over a bus, but the driver shook his fist at her because all his passengers got out of the bus to watch her.

She jumped over an apple tree, but the farmer shouted at her when she knocked all his best apples on to the ground.

She jumped over a cloud, but she kicked it by mistake and it rained all over the countryside. People were very annoyed.

She jumped over a church steeple and disturbed the weather-cock.

'Go away,' he said. 'You're being a nuisance. Why don't you try jumping over the sun for a change?'

So the cow tried to jump over the sun, but it was much too hot, and she thought her feet might melt. She came down to rest in a lovely cool field of sweet, green grass and juicy buttercups.

'This is the place for me,' said the cow.

She looked up at the moon in the sky and decided never to go jumping again.

'Not even over the stars,' thought the cow sleepily. 'They're much too pretty to knock out of the sky.'

Rider on the wind

I ride the wind, I climb the sky,
I touch the clouds that sail so high.
I hear them call, 'Come, come away,
Forget the world that bids you stay.'
The wind sweeps down to capture me.
I cannot wait to be set free!
I toss my head, my tail streams wide,
I prance and leap, I snatch and glide,
But all my struggles are in vain—
My master's hand is on my rein.

What am I?

Koogee the lost kitten

Pepi was crying. She was very sad because the pretty Persian kitten, that she was given for her fourth birthday, was nowhere to be found.

Pepi and her father had searched in the gardens and in the woods around their home.

Now it was almost tea-time and they had been looking for Koogee the kitten all day.

Pepi's mother made tea, but Pepi couldn't eat anything because she was so worried about her pet.

'He has never been away before,' cried Pepi. 'Wherever can he be.'

'We'll look again after tea,' said her Father.

It was almost dark when Pepi and Father returned home. Mother met them at the door.

'We haven't found him,' sobbed Pepi and she went upstairs and climbed into bed, the tears still trickling down her cheeks.

'M-e-e-o-w, m-e-e-o-w.' Pepi sat up in bed and switched on the light.

'M-e-e-o-w, m-e-e-o-w.' There it was again. Pepi jumped out of bed.

The cries came from her toy cupboard. She opened the cupboard door and there, sitting with the toys, was Koogee.

Pepi picked him up. 'What a silly little kitten!' she whispered, holding him tight.

Six hidden parcels

I bought my Christmas presents, and I
hid them all away.
I didn't want them found and opened
up before today.
But now it's Christmas morning, and
I'm very sad to tell—
I cannot find them anywhere! I've
hidden them too well.
My children want their parcels, and
I don't know what to do,
So can you find six for me now? I
would be pleased with you!

Looking after baby

'Look after Baby, won't you Lionel,' said Mrs Fairweather as she left the pram and went into the baker's shop.

Lionel the Golden Retriever was very proud of his new and important position in the Fairweather family. His job was to watch over their bouncy baby. Frankie the cat helped sometimes too.

Baby Fairweather sat up in his pram, his bright little eyes darting about the street. He was very bouncy indeed this morning, so bouncy in fact that he rocked the pram until it began to edge its way along the pavement. Lionel ran up and down, barking his head off, but he couldn't stop the pram.

With a WHIZZ-WHIZZ of its wheels, it was off down the steep hill, baby and all, with Lionel and Mrs Fairweather racing after it.

'Oh, we'll never catch it,' gasped Mrs Fairweather as the pram hurtled on down the road.

But they did – and do you know where? In their very own front garden. The pram had sailed smoothly right through the front gate. Baby Fairweather was gurgling with laughter when they found him.

When Mrs Fairweather had taken him inside, Lionel sat down panting on the doorstep and quietly admitted to Frankie, 'I'll be glad when he grows up, you know. It's very tiring looking after babies.'

And Frankie agreed.

The lion and the mule

Deep in the forest lived a lion and a mule. The lion thought he was very clever and that the mule was rather stupid.

One day they saw a carpenter building a house. 'That is a very fine house,' said the lion.

The carpenter was very frightened when he saw the lion, but he said, 'I will make you a house fit for the king of all the beasts. Come back tomorrow and it will be ready.'

The next day the lion went to see his new house. 'Just creep inside and see how well it fits,' said the carpenter.

The lion crept inside and the carpenter said, 'I have just got to put a few more nails in the door.' He quickly nailed up the end of the big box he had made and the lion was trapped inside. Then he hurried off to get help.

Then along came the mule. 'How do you like your new house?' he asked.

'The carpenter has made it too small and I can't get out,' said the lion.

The mule chuckled because the lion had been tricked. But he kicked the box hard, splintering the wood with his strong, hind feet. The lion crept out and the two ran away.

The lion never again said that he was more clever than the mule and the two animals became friends.

Mystery of the missing animals

The keeper looked so worried
When we visited the zoo.
'I did have lots of animals
That I would have shown to you.'

'Please Mr Keeper, do not despair,
Look harder – your animals really
are there.'

So, if in this picture you look deeper,
You'll see six animals hiding from
the keeper.

Peter and Jolly

Peter was collecting dandelion leaves for his rabbit. He climbed a gate into a field to look for some more.

Suddenly, something pushed his shoulder and he jumped with fright.

There, looming over the back of him, stood an enormous carthorse.

'N-nice horse,' he gasped, edging away slowly. The huge animal, slowly followed him.

Peter clutched his dandelion leaves harder, and moved faster, backwards.

The horse moved faster, too!

Peter gave a cry and turned and ran.

But the faster he went, the faster went the horse! Thankfully Peter reached the gate, and flung himself over it, falling in a heap. The horse stopped and swung his long neck over the gate, pushing Peter again. Peter gulped. Then he heard a munching sound. Oh dear – was it eating him? He felt a tug at his hand and scrambled up. Then he stared in surprise.

The horse was eating his dandelion leaves. It didn't want to eat him at all.

At that moment, a man walked up. 'You *are* kind,' he laughed, 'to feed my Jolly his favourite leaves.'

Peter shakily held out the leaves to Jolly who snorted 'Thank you' – and ate them all up. Peter was surprised that such a big horse liked the same food as his rabbit!

Witch magic

Emily watched the rain through her bedroom window. 'What a dull day. I hope tomorrow is more exciting.' A sound came from the cupboard. Emily looked – the broom must have toppled over.

As Emily opened the door, the broomstick hopped out! It flew around scattering clouds of blue dust. The dust cleared, and there stood a strange old lady.

'Hello,' she said cheerily. 'Would you like to see some magic?'

'Yes, please!' said Emily.

The old lady sat astride her broomstick. 'Jump on!' she called. Emily sat behind and held tightly. *Whoosh*, out of the window they flew – higher and higher, faster and faster.

'Look!' cried the old lady. She waved her wand and stars came out, shimmering brightly in the sky.

'Look!' cried the old lady. She waved her wand. A magnificent castle appeared in the clouds. Fairies flew to greet them. They sang to beautiful music and danced on silver moonbeams.

'Time to go,' whispered the old lady. Instantly, Emily found herself alone in her bedroom. 'Have I been dreaming?' she wondered.

Fun at the farm

Tom Turnip the scarecrow wanted to help the farmer, who couldn't be outside working because he was indoors searching for his wife's ring, which she had lost that morning.

So Tom left the corn field where he always stood to scare away the birds, and hopped to the pig-sty.

'You need a bath,' said Tom to the muddy pigs, and found a wash-tub of soapy water by the kitchen door.

The pigs liked being washed. They rolled about in the bubbles and Tom scrubbed them hard. Then he opened the gate of the pig-sty and let the pigs into the field to run about and get dry.

Just as the farmer came out looking very cross with Tom, a magpie flew from the corn field and swooped down to the farmyard. It picked something shiny and hard out of the soap bubbles.

'My ring!' cried the farmer's wife, coming outside. 'It must have fallen from my finger into the wash-tub!'

The farmer forgave Tom but made him promise he would never open farm gates again. Then they all helped chase the clean pink pigs back into their sty and Tom went back to his field.

Tired Tina

Tina jumped up and down excitedly. She was going to the zoo.

Mummy laughed, 'You'll be tired! There's lots of walking to do.'

Tina's feet hurt by the time they reached the monkeys, but she laughed as they swung about their cage.

Tina's legs ached as she watched the penguins. They looked so funny waddling round the pool.

Tina sighed as she climbed the hill to the polar bears, but she clapped as they frolicked in the water.

Tina was tired at the chimpanzees' tea party, but she giggled as they poured tea all over themselves.

'Would you like to ride on a camel?' asked Mummy.

Tina nodded, too weary to speak.

The camel swayed along the paths. Tina smiled – this was fun and she could see all the animals in the zoo from her seat on the camel's back.

Tina yawned as she got into bed that night, 'You know, Mummy, I feel as though I'm still on that funny old camel.'

But that didn't stop her from falling fast asleep.

Lucy Bodkin and the wallpaper

One day when it was dull and wet outside, a funny little lady called Lucy Bodkin decided to do something cheerful indoors. She would put up some bright new wallpaper.

'I'll do the wall around the window,' she said.

Very soon that funny little lady was bustling about getting everything ready. Chair to stand on for the high places. Saucepan for paste. Spoon to stir the paste. Big brush to slosh it on with.

'But I haven't any wallpaper,' thought Lucy sadly. Suddenly, she remembered the huge book of wallpaper patterns in her cupboard and it gave her a wonderful idea. If she cut every page from that wallpaper book she could paste them on the wall one by one.

Lucy Bodkin worked very hard, then she stood back, looked happily at her handiwork and thought her wall as smart as ever a wall could be. There was every sort and shape of pattern you could imagine.

'It reminds me of a beautiful patchwork quilt with a window in the middle,' said the funny little lady.

The vet

'Can you get in?'
Said the vet with a grin.
'I'm so busy I'm in a spin!
Pam's parrot swallowed a carrot,
Shirley's sheep's asleep in a heap,
Andy's cat unravelled a mat,
David's dog growled at a frog,
Henry's fish jumped out of a dish,
I hope your mouse —
Won't run round the house.'
'My mouse is good,' I was going to say,
And then I found he'd run away!

Can you find him?

Adolphus the leopard

Adolphus is a leopard
Who thought he'd change his spots.
He bought a tin of yellow paint
To cover all the dots.

But no one seems to know him,
So he sits and longs for rain,
Just hoping that a heavy shower
Will bring his spots again.

The garden gnome

A garden gnome stood on a flower bed and felt very bored and lonely. All day long he looked at the trees and the weeds and got wet when it rained and too hot in the summer.

'I wish I had a spade, I could help clear the garden of weeds,' he said.

Just then a friendly squirrel was passing and, hearing the gnome's wish, he went and told the fairy who granted wishes.

'That's easy,' said the fairy. 'I'll go and see him tonight.'

When it was dark the fairy went to see the gnome. In her hand she carried a tiny garden spade.

'Here you are,' she said as she gave him the spade, 'but remember you can only work when everyone else is asleep, for you mustn't ever be seen digging.'

'Thank you very much,' said the gnome. 'I'll remember what you say.'

So every night now he's happy, digging away and tidying the garden. But by daylight he's still in the same place and his spade hidden in the leaves somewhere. And the people whose garden it is can't understand why in that part of the garden the weeds don't grow.

Playtime in Toyland

It was midnight. The door of the toy cupboard opened very quietly, and Teddy Bear looked out.

'It's all right,' he whispered. 'There's nobody about.'

Out tumbled the toys. There were dolls, farm animals, soft cuddly toys and Ben the red engine. 'All aboard for Dreamland,' he puffed, and the small toys jumped inside.

Off they went, while Teddy, Panda and the dolls danced to the tunes from the musical box.

'This is better than sleeping in that horrid dark cupboard,' said Teddy.

Then Ben and his passengers came back. Suddenly, Panda shouted, 'Into the cupboard – someone's coming.'

In two shakes of Lambkin's tail, everyone was back except poor Teddy who wasn't quick enough. The cupboard door slammed, and he was left outside.

Next morning, Mary picked Teddy up from the floor. 'What were you doing last night Teddy?' she whispered. 'I know I put you away, but you don't like that cupboard very much, do you? You mustn't be afraid. I'll put you by my bed tonight, and you can share my night-light. You'll like that won't you?'

Teddy gave a happy little grunt.

Going home

The streets are busy, full of noise
From all the laughing girls and boys.
Now school has ended for the day,
They've started running home to play.

Their tea is waiting, ready laid,
With toast and cake that mummy's
  made.
First everybody starts to talk,
The dog jumps up and wants a walk.
Then later, toys are packed away
And bedtime ends a happy day.

Claude goes climbing

One fine morning, Claude's mother stretched and jumped up to sit on the window-sill in the sun. 'Today is the start of spring,' she said, 'so I shall take you into the garden and teach you all to climb.'

'Now kittens, watch me carefully,' she said, and she climbed up the garden gate with her sharp claws. The kittens concentrated hard. Next she scrambled up onto the roof of the garden shed. Then she took a leap straight up the trellis where the honey-suckle grew on the side of the house. 'Now I will teach you,' she said. She showed the kittens how to sharpen their claws, and how to cling and clamber. The kittens struggled up an apple tree one by one and soon they were doing very well.

'Very good,' said their mother, and then seeing Tabby Tim the cat who lived next-door, she went to talk to him. 'Stay and play until I come back,' she said to the kittens. And off she went.

The kittens played and waited. They played 'Catch the Cat' (a sort of tag) and 'Hunt the Kipper' and then Celestine said 'I have an idea. Let's go and practise our climbing.'

Claude thought it was a good idea, so off they went. They had a race with Claude and Chloe climbing one tree and Clive and Celestine climbing another.

Celestine and Clive soon reached the top of theirs but Claude and Chloe still had a long way to go because their tree was taller. 'Let's stop now,' said Chloe, but Claude didn't want to, and he climbed on. Chloe sat on her branch and waited. 'Claude,' she cried, 'come back!' but Claude carried on climbing.

'You'll slip,' called careful Clive. Claude was level with the top of the house now. He could see the birds in their nests and Mrs Plum making beds in the bed-rooms. And still he carried on climbing.

Soon Claude called, 'I'm at the top,' and he was.

He waved. The other kittens wailed. 'You'll fall!' they cried, and they put their paws over their eyes.

Just at that moment their mother came back. She saw the kittens staring up at the sky. 'Claude! However did you climb up there? You'll fall!'

Claude purred with pride. 'I'm purrfectly safe,' he said. 'I'll come down soon.'

To tell the truth, poor Claude was stuck, so he pretended that he didn't want to come down.

At supper time Mr Plum strolled into the garden to look at the sky, and suddenly he caught sight of Claude. 'That silly kitten is stuck,' he said and he hurried to fetch a ladder. But the ladder was too short, so Mr Plum called the Fire Brigade.

All at once there was a screech of brakes and a big red van stopped outside the house – it was a fire engine. 'We'll soon have him down, sir!' called a fireman climbing up the ladder. He caught hold of Claude, popped him into his pocket and down the ladder they came! Poor Claude was very cold. He had to be taken into the kitchen for some warm milk, and the fireman had a cup of tea and a piece of cake.

'Claude,' said his mother, severely, 'you must be more careful. Firemen are for fighting fires, not collecting kittens caught in trees.'

But Claude was so tired he didn't hear – he had fallen asleep!

The proud oak

There grew in a wood an old oak;
So twisted was he
That this arrogant tree
Never spoke.

The beeches and elms laughed aloud;
But with branches held high
He just stared at the sky,
Grim and proud.

A sapling ash grew near his root;
For the oak every gaze
Was of wonder and praise,
From this shoot.

Let the elm trees and beeches all laugh;
The oak swelled with pride
Till his timbers inside
Split in half!

A pal for Pansy

Pansy was a little grey and white kitten, who belonged to Claire. Pansy was very fond of Claire, and liked to follow her everywhere. One day, she followed Claire to school, and one of the bigger children had to bring Pansy home again. Another time, Pansy followed Claire all the way to her cousin Paula's house.

When Claire's Daddy said one evening that he wanted to have a puppy as well as a kitten, Claire's Mummy sighed.

'I think we have enough trouble as it is, with Pansy following Claire everywhere,' said Mum. 'A puppy would be extra trouble.'

Daddy wanted a puppy very much indeed, and so did Claire, so at last Mummy agreed.

Pansy was a little worried when a small, brown puppy came to live with them, but she soon found that the puppy was lots of fun. His name was Pete, and he loved games. Pansy and Pete played 'chase-tails' and 'catch-me-if-you-can' and 'hide-and-seek'. Pansy grew very fond of her new pal. Of course, she was still fond of Claire, but now that she had someone else to play with, there was no need to follow Claire everywhere.

Mummy was pleased that Pansy was no longer being any trouble, and she was very pleased that she had agreed to have Puppy Pete, after all.

The magic safety-pin

Miss Trill thought her voice was quite superb, so she planned to sing at her birthday party in her best dress. In her excitement she caught her foot in the hem and mended it with a safety-pin.

Special safety-pins look much like ordinary ones, so Miss Trill had no idea this was a magic one. When she sang everyone yawned. After many wrong notes the safety-pin popped open, startled Miss Trill and stopped her trilling!

Hubert her nephew found the safety-pin. He was a lazy boy, and he wanted to miss cricket, so he put a bandage on his leg and held it in place with the safety-pin. But at school it popped open and bandaged Hubert's leg to his chair. How everyone laughed when he tried to get up!

The cleaner found the safety-pin. She threw it in the dustbin, which was emptied on the town dump. There it winked at a passing magpie, who flew off with it.

Now the magic safety-pin is having a rest from adventuring – he is holding together a scarecrow's coat in a field of young barley.

The wedding day

James and Susannah were very lucky because they had a big sister called Judith, who was really quite a lot older than them.

Very soon Judith was going to get married in a church, in a long white dress. Quite naturally she had chosen Susannah to be her bridesmaid and James to be her pageboy.

For weeks Judith had been busy in the evenings sewing her own wedding dress, and Susannah was quite sure her big sister was going to look as pretty as any princess in her dress and train of pure white lace. Her posy was going to be a mixture of pink, white and blue flowers and those were the colours of Susannah's bridesmaid dress.

On the morning of the wedding, Mother helped Judith into her wedding dress and arranged her veil and train, while Aunty Kit helped Susannah and James into their outfits.

Before they knew it, it was time to leave for the church. And after the ceremony, when Judith was married to her new husband, Bob, everyone gathered outside the church in the bright sunshine to have their photograph taken.

Susannah and James had never enjoyed a day so much – it was certainly a day to remember!

The vain Siamese cat

There was once a Siamese cat called Shantung who was very vain.

Every day she went to admire her reflection in the pond in the wood. The frogs who lived in the pond laughed at her and said, 'One day, you won't look so beautiful.'

But Shantung answered, 'I don't believe you,' and flicked her tail in defiance.

So the frogs made a plan to stop her being so vain. The very next day they hid themselves in the long grass round the pond, and they waited.

Along came Shantung and she spent some time admiring herself. Suddenly all the frogs croaked and stamped their feet and made such a noise that Shantung lost her balance and fell – PLOP – into the water. The pond was shallow and she quickly scrambled out, miaowing loudly.

How the frogs laughed! Poor Shantung looked a sight – her wet fur made her look so skinny and her whiskers drooped. She didn't stop running until she reached home and it took ages for her fur to dry.

But the frogs' plan had worked and Shantung never went back to look at herself in the pond again.

Fishing

I've fished in the river,
I've fished in the sea,
I've fished before breakfast
And long after tea.
I can honestly say
That of fishing I'm fond,
But I caught my best fish
In the old village pond.

    Its scales were pure silver,
Its fins were bright gold,
Its tail rainbow-coloured,
A joy to behold.
It gazed at me sadly,
(Its eyes were jet-black).
It looked so unhappy
I threw it straight back.

The striped scarf

Mr Tibbit, the zoo keeper, loved animals, and so did his wife, Mrs Tibbit. One day, she took all the wool left over from other knitting she had done. There were all the colours of the rainbow. She began to knit busily.

'I am making you a striped scarf!' she smiled at Mr Tibbit, but he was very worried. The colours clashed so!

The scarf grew longer and longer and LONGER, coiling on the floor like a bright striped snake.

At last, Mrs Tibbit cast off her stitches. 'There,' she declared.

'Thank you,' Mr Tibbit smiled weakly. 'I shall wear it at once.'

'I was only teasing you, my dear,' chuckled Mrs Tibbit. 'The scarf is for Geraldine the Giraffe. With that long neck, she gets such bad sore throats in the winter.'

Mr Tibbit went and wrapped the scarf round and round Geraldine's neck, and the giraffe was delighted. She didn't mind a bit about the colours clashing.

'You are clever, my dear,' Mr Tibbit beamed at his wife. And Geraldine the Giraffe thought so, too.

The sad little Princess

Long ago, in a golden castle, lived a sad little Princess. The Princess never smiled.

The servants at the castle tried to make the little Princess happy. 'I hate porridge,' snapped the Princess. 'Take it away and bring me some icecream.'

The Cook would obey, and hurry to the kitchen.

Behind the Castle was a beautiful garden and the Princess used to watch the gardener planting rose trees.

'Don't touch,' warned the gardener one day, 'the thorns are sharp.'

But the Princess took hold of a rose. 'Ouch,' she squealed, 'that tree pricked my finger. Get rid of it,' she ordered.

Just at that moment, a beautiful fairy appeared. 'What a cross-patch!' said the Fairy. 'I think it's time you learned how to be happy.'

The Princess smiled just a little and said, 'Please tell me how.'

'Go now and look into the waters of the beautiful lake,' replied the fairy.

The Princess did as the fairy said. Looking into the smooth water, she saw a happy, smiling face. It was her own.

By the time she turned round, the fairy had gone without another word. And from that day on the Princess was the happiest person in the world and she never forgot that beautiful fairy.

Bubbles

Bubbles, bubbles, in the bath,
Ten rising here and there;
How many bubbles have to burst
To leave SIX in the air?

Eight big bubbles floating,
And sinking to the floor;
How many bubbles vanished there
To leave you only FOUR?

One large bubble by itself,
As lonely as can be;
How many bubbles must you blow
To make the bubbles THREE?

Alexander's magic soap

It was Alexander's bath night, which was just as well because his knees were the grubbiest in the world! He stepped into the bath and then plopped three boats and a deep-sea diver into the water. There was a smiling yellow duck too, but he had to stay on the shelf above the taps. His name was Soapy Duck because every bit of him was made of lovely yellow soap and Alexander didn't use him in case he wore out.

'Don't forget to wash those grubby knees,' Mummy called from the other room.

'All right,' replied Alexander. But instead he made a harbour for his boats. Later he played at looking for sharks with his deep-sea diver.

And then something quite magical happened:

'Quack-quack!' came a voice from the shelf. It was Soapy Duck and as he spoke he toppled over and landed with a splash in the bath water.

'Hey, you'll get wet!' said Alexander.

'Quack! Ducks like being wet,' answered Soapy Duck. He had a wonderful time swimming and splashing around the bath and when it was time to come out he was exactly the same size and shape as he was when he went in.

Presently, Mummy called again. 'How about those knees?'

'They're done,' replied Alexander. 'Soapy Duck did them for me.'

Humpty Dumpty

Before you fall off that wall,
Pray, Humpty, choose your fate—
Poached, made into an omelet,
Or with bacon on a plate?

Adolphus and his friends

Adolphus was a dolphin. He lived in the sea. One of his neighbours was Soapy-Sea-Monster. Adolphus and his friends decided that the sea-bed would be a happier place without Soapy because he swallowed little fishes. 'But how shall we make him go?' asked Harry Haddock.

Now all dolphins are clever and wise, and Adolphus was wisest of all. There was one place in the Deep Sea Forest which only he knew. No one but he had ever gone there. So one day he swam up to Soapy and whispered, 'I know a place where there are thousands of little fat fishes all begging to be swallowed up.'

'Lead me to it,' said greedy old Soapy. Soapy followed Adolphus in and out of a hundred caverns and a thousand mazes. Then, becoming impatient, he hurried on in front of Adolphus.

This was what the dolphin had been waiting for, and he dodged behind a sea-tangle-tree while Soapy swam on . . . and on . . . and on . . . Adolphus returned to his friends and told them, 'Soapy is lost forever in the Deep Sea Forest. He will never bother us again.'

And all the fish of the sea shouted 'HURRAH!'

Polly's peculiar pen

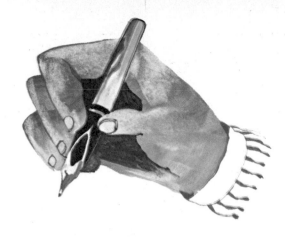

Polly Perks had a peculiar pen. It looked as if it were an ordinary pen but ordinary it was not.

One day Polly wrote a shopping list for her mother but instead of *one pound of butter*, the pen wrote *one pound of sausages*. Instead of *one packet of cornflakes*, it wrote *one enormous cabbage*!

When Polly's mother saw what Polly had brought from the supermarket she cried, 'Oh Polly! Why did you write sausages and cabbage when I quite plainly told you butter and cornflakes?'

'*I* didn't write the list,' said Polly. 'The pen did. It's a *very* peculiar pen.'

'Yes it is,' agreed Mrs Perks, 'so we will get rid of it,' and she dropped the peculiar pen into the rubbish bin.

But the peculiar pen rolled out of the rubbish bin and along to Polly's room.

'Hi,' said the pen to Polly, 'we weren't very clever, were we?'

'No, we weren't,' Polly agreed and as she spoke, Mrs Perks came into the room. Seeing the pen, she exclaimed, 'What is that pen doing here? I threw it into the rubbish bin.'

'W-e-e-ell,' said Polly, 'it has promised never to write the wrong things again.'

And from that day on, the peculiar pen wrote down only those things which Mrs Perks had ordered.

Naughty Robbie

Robbie the little white puppy loved to play with Richard in the garden.

One day they went to a field, and had to cross two roads. Robbie was unhappy on his lead and as soon as Richard let him go, he thought, 'How dare he put me on a lead,' and ran off into the long grass.

Richard called and called, but Robbie didn't come.

'Where can he be?' thought Richard. 'I shall throw a stick. He loves bringing it back to me.' He tossed it many times, but still Robbie didn't come.

Poor Robbie was lost. He had meant to run only a little way, but the grass was so tall he couldn't see. He ran so far he didn't hear Richard calling him and he was very scared.

A big dog came along and sniffed at Robbie: 'Lost are you? You puppies are all the same. You run too far. Follow me,' and he bounded through the grass.

Robbie saw Richard. 'Woof! Woof! Here I am,' he yelped.

Richard hugged him. 'Don't you ever run off again,' he said.

Cat

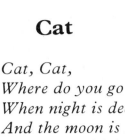

Cat, Cat,
Where do you go
When night is deep
And the moon is low?
Do you go visiting
Other cats?
Do you chase mice or go
Hunting rats?
OR
Do you fly
To the midnight sky
Through the yellow gloom
On a witch's broom?

The late cuckoo

Two cuckoos lived in a clock and they took it in turns to cuckoo the time. No one would ever have known there were two cuckoos living there because they were exactly alike – except that one cuckoo was always on time while the other was always late.

'I'm sorry,' he said to his brother, 'I will be on time when it's my turn next,' but of course he wasn't.

It was very annoying for the punctual cuckoo, so he decided to think of a way to help his brother. 'I know,' he said, 'I will set the kitchen timer to go *ping* two minutes before you have to go through the door to shout the time.'

That's what he did, and when the timer went *ping* the late cuckoo stopped what he was doing and hurried to the door and at the top of his voice shouted his cuckoos.

And he was never late again.

Sam Spider and Sebastian Snail

'I wish I had a house like yours to live in,' said Sam Spider to Sebastian Snail, looking at Sebastian's shell.

'And I wish I could weave a web like yours to live in,' said Sebastian.

'Look, there's a walnut shell,' Sam said. 'I can make a house out of that.'

'And here's a reel of cotton,' said Sebastian. 'I'll weave myself a web.'

Sam just managed to lift the shell, and crawl under it – but then he couldn't get out.

'It's dark in here,' he called. 'Sebastian, help me out. I don't like this house.'

But Sebastian had started to unwind the cotton to make a web, and he'd got all tangled up. 'I can't move,' he said.

Just then, Charlie the Kitten came along, and started to play with the walnut shell. He turned it over, and Sam crawled out and scampered back to his web. Then Charlie pushed the cotton-reel with his paw, and it rolled along, pulling the cotton off Sebastian.

'I don't want a house, now,' said Sam.

'And I don't want a web,' said Sebastian.

'Thanks, Charlie,' they both said, but the kitten didn't hear – he was running about in a tree, pretending to be a tiger . . .

Shy little mouse

*Deep in the roots of this tree lives a
    mouse,*
Hidden away in her snug little house.
*When her pantry is empty she creeps
    softly out*
*For berries and nuts when there's no
    one about.*
But if she hears even the tiniest sound,
*She scurries away to her home
    underground.*
*If you look very carefully, perhaps you
    will see*
*That mouse peeping out from her house
    in the tree.*

Billy and the baby dragon

Billy had found a baby dragon in the woods. He asked Dad if the dragon could come and live with them, but Dad laughed and said, 'Certainly not.'

So Billy made up his mind. He took a bag of apples and a slice of gooseberry pie, and hurried to the woods.

'I'm going to take you to the zoo today,' he told the dragon.

The dragon *HUFFED*, and swallowed the apples and gooseberry pie.

It was a long walk to the zoo, and when they got there they were met by an important-looking man.

'What have you got there?' he asked.

'A baby dragon, and he hasn't anywhere to live,' replied Billy.

The man was delighted. There had never been a dragon in the zoo.

'Why,' he said, 'if he'll stay with us, we'll build him a special house, and you can come and see him whenever you like.'

So the baby dragon lived happily in the zoo and every Saturday, Billy's Dad took Billy in the car to see him.

Of course, the baby dragon grew very, very big. But Billy always remembered to take him a bag of apples, and a slice of gooseberry pie.

The tumbledown cottage

Joanne wandered down a lane picking wild flowers until she came to a tumble-down cottage, with the door open. She could see right inside to a cosy room, with shining copper, and old furniture.

Then she saw a white-haired old lady, staring back over spectacles on her nose.

Joanne blushed. 'Would you like my flowers?' she asked.

The old lady smiled and thanked her very much for the flowers. She said she was Mrs Hubbard.

She gave Joanne the nicest drink she had ever tasted. There was cherry tart and golden scones to eat, and the sweetest little brown and white dog that did tricks. The old lady made him beg for a bone. Joanne enjoyed her visit so much that she was sorry to say goodbye.

Her Mummy laughed when she heard her tale. 'Why,' she said, 'it sounds just like an Old Mother Hubbard story!'

'Of *course*!' exclaimed Joanne. 'That's just who it was!' Then she added thoughtfully, 'But that nursery rhyme has it all wrong, you know.'

Uncle Carpenter's climbing frame

Luke and his sister Lucy had an uncle who liked making things. They called him Uncle Carpenter because, as Mummy said, he was very good with wood. When Luke and Lucy were tiny he made them trollies to push and trucks to pull, and tricycles to ride.

When Luke and Lucy were older, Uncle Carpenter made them a climbing frame, and Luke and Lucy thought it was wonderful. There were wooden ladders for climbing up and down, and two wooden platforms for climbing up to and down from.

One day, they pretended that they were sailors, and their climbing frame became a ship. The grass became their sea, and they had lots of adventures.

Another time, the climbing frame became a dolls' house, with a room upstairs and down. Luke and Lucy pretended that they were dolls who lived inside it.

One morning, they decided that their climbing frame was a double-decker bus, and that afternoon, it became their train. Once it was a shop where Luke and Lucy sold pretend things to their friends.

'You didn't just give them a climbing frame, Uncle Carpenter,' laughed Mummy. 'You gave them a ship, a house, a bus, a train and a shop!'

Socks for Cedric Centipede

As soon as the weather turned cold, Cedric Centipede began to feel cold too, especially his feet! Cedric had lots of feet – a hundred, in fact – and when they were all cold, Cedric was miserable.

'I would knit Cedric some green socks, but I only have enough wool for one pair,' said Sadie Ladybird.

'I would knit him some blue socks,' said Myrtle Beetle, 'but I only have enough wool for one pair.'

'I know!' said Sadie Ladybird, suddenly. 'I'll knit a green pair, you knit a blue pair, and we'll ask every woodland lady to knit a pair of socks with whatever wool they have. If we ask enough ladies, we'll have enough socks. Cedric will need fifty pairs.'

Myrtle Beetle and Sadie Ladybird hurried around the wood to talk to Heidi Spider, Vera Earwig, Cilla Caterpillar and other ladies they knew.

Soon, fifty little ladies were busy knitting. By the end of a week, they came to Cedric Centipede, one by one, each with a parcel. In each parcel, Cedric found a pair of socks. There were green socks, blue socks, pink socks, yellow socks, brown socks, orange socks – in fact socks of every colour you can think of. Oh, Cedric was delighted!

Daffy and the fallen moon

Daffy was the silliest elf in the whole wood. Ossie the Owl was always scolding him. 'You just don't *think* hard enough,' said Ossie.

One day some boys and girls were playing with some balloons in a meadow beyond the wood. Suddenly the wind caught a big, yellow balloon and it blew away, over the trees.

That night Daffy was coming home very late. It was dark and he could hardly see the path. 'Oh, dear!' he sighed. 'I wonder where the moon is tonight?'

He looked up at the sky and then he saw something in the branches of a tree. It was the yellow balloon. But Daffy didn't know that. 'Goodness,' he cried, 'the moon's fallen out of the sky!'

Daffy climbed up the tree and untangled the balloon string from the branches. Then he hurried home. 'Ossie,' he cried, 'the moon's fallen out of the sky. How can I put it back again?'

Ossie laughed so much he nearly fell off the branch where he was sitting. 'Look up there,' he said. The moon was just peeping out from behind the clouds.

'It was hiding all the time,' said Daffy. But he didn't really mind Ossie laughing at him, because he'd got a lovely big balloon to play with.

Sophie's special doll

Sophie was nearly five-years old, and she was about to start school. She was excited about it – but she had one worry.

'Who will look after Baby Doll, Teddy and Bunny, while I'm at school all day?' she asked.

'I'll look after them,' said Mum.

Sophie knew that Mum was already busy all day looking after Sophie's little brother, Christopher, and her little sister, Victoria.

'You haven't time to look after my toys,' said Sophie.

Mum could see that Sophie was worried. Then, on the day before Sophie's fifth birthday, Mum found the answer. She was looking in the toy shop, wondering what to buy for Sophie, when she saw a pretty doll, dressed as a nurse. She bought the doll, and she gave it to Sophie on her fifth birthday.

As Sophie unwrapped her parcel, Mum said, 'This is Nurse Doll. She has come to live with you, so that she can look after your younger dolls while you are at school.'

Sophie was delighted!

Nurse Doll looked a grown-up sort of doll – sensible and kind.

'I'm sure she will look after Baby Doll, Teddy and Bunny very nicely indeed,' said Sophie. 'Now I can go to school every morning without having to worry about leaving my toys.'

Upsidedown farm

The dog is in the hutch
He doesn't like it much.
The horse is in the sty
I can't imagine why!
In the kennel lies the pig
It's lucky he's not very big.
The rabbit runs off to the stable
Just as fast as he is able.

It's nearly time now for their tea –
Tell them all where they should be!

Ben and the tractor

The shiny new tractor arrived at the farm just as Mrs Buckle was talking to Farmer Jones.

Ben the old farm horse stood by the gate and listened.

'Yes,' Farmer Jones said, 'you can have Ben. I don't need him to pull the plough anymore. I've got this new tractor.'

'Oh, splendid,' said Mrs Buckle, 'the children do so want to ride in their new cart, but we haven't a horse big enough to pull it.'

So that was settled.

Poor old Ben. He scowled at the tractor. 'I'm not needed anymore, thanks to you,' he neighed, and galloped off down the field feeling very sad.

The next morning, Farmer Jones hitched Ben to the cart, then he went off on his new tractor. Ben trotted down the lane with the children singing behind him.

'Why,' he thought, 'this is fun. It's much nicer than pulling a plough.'

On the way home they met Farmer Jones. He was very cross. 'That tractor has got itself stuck in a ditch,' he complained. 'I need Ben to pull it out.'

'Hooray,' whinnied Ben, 'so I am useful after all. Silly tractor!'

The Station Master's garden

The Station Master of Cobbletown was pruning his roses.

'What a shame!' he cried, reading the letter Postman had brought. 'They are closing my station. There will be no more trains after this week.'

'Oh dear,' sighed Postman. 'There will be no summer passengers to see your lovely garden.'

Even though the Station Master knew that the train would come into his station and leave for the last time on Saturday, he still weeded and planted and pruned.

On Saturday the townspeople came to wave goodbye to the last train.

As it chugged into the station and came to a halt in front of the beautiful garden, everyone gasped. Down the steps of the train came the Queen of Poggleland!

She had decided to take a train ride.

'What a lovely garden!' she exclaimed. 'Your summer passengers will enjoy it.'

'But they are closing my Railway Station, Your Majesty,' said the Station Master with a deep bow. 'There will be no summer visitors.'

'Nonsense!' exclaimed the Queen. 'I command that it remains open for all to see your garden.'

Mother and Susan's lodging house

The bathtub certainly made a funny noise when mother pulled out the plug. As she stood there drying Susan with a towel, they heard a loud 'burble.'

Both Mother and Susan leaned over to look down the bathtub drain. They saw a funny little creature no bigger than Susan's thumb singing in the water.

'Surprised?' it asked. 'I'm Burbler. Someone has to make the burbling noises when the bathtub water runs out. Have you heard Cousin Gurgler in the wash-basin?'

Mother filled the wash-basin with water then pulled the plug to drain it. 'Gurgle, gurgle, gurgle.' Another little creature, even smaller than Burbler, stuck its head out of the drain and gurgled. 'Have you seen Uncle Squeaker and Auntie Creaker?' it asked looking up.

'Where are they?' Mother and Susan asked in surprise.

'Creaker lives in the floorboards and Squeaker lives under the stairs. Listen for them when you walk around,' Gurgler answered. 'Their job is to make noise too.'

'What a lodging house we live in!' Mother and Susan laughed. 'Maybe we ought to start charging rent.'

Singaway Sue

Singaway Sue,
What does she do?
She doesn't wash dishes
Or bake, boil, or brew.
She'll not write a letter,
She won't read a book,
She'll not make a bed —
She refuses to cook.

Oh, Singaway Sue,
What does she do?
She sings and she s-i-n-g-s
And she s--i--n--g--s all day through.

Gay's birthday party

It was Gay's birthday. As she put on her pretty dress, the doorbell rang. Her guests had arrived and they'd brought the most exciting parcels with them.

They all sat down to tea. 'Wish!' they cried when they saw the birthday cake with the four pink candles. Gay p-u-f-f-e-d, and blew them all out at once.

'It will come true now,' smiled Mummy.

Gay opened her presents – there was a big box of paints, a book to colour, a pretty bag and lots more.

When she had finished, Auntie Joan said, 'Come into the kitchen. I have a present for you, too.'

Gay stood in the doorway. The sweetest little black kitten sat there.

'Oh!' she gasped. 'That's just what I wished for,' and she ran and picked him up.

Later, when the party was over, she tried to think of a name for her kitten, but she couldn't.

She went to say goodnight and when she saw him she stared – the little kitten was completely white. He had upset his saucer of milk all over himself.

'What a pickle!' Daddy laughed.

'That's it, I shall call him Pickles!' said Gay, and Pickles purred loudly.

Captain Kiddo's surprise

Captain Kiddo anchored his pirate ship off the tropical island.

'Ho, you scum of the Seven Seas,' he shouted to his men, 'put my chest in the longboat. We all go ashore here.'

His crew lifted the big chest into the longboat. Then they rowed ashore. Soft, golden sand crunched beneath their sea boots as they pulled the boat up on the beach. Gulls circled overhead. Four of the strongest pirates heaved the chest onto their shoulders while Captain Kiddo studied his map.

'Follow me up Spyglass Hill, you swabs,' he growled.

On the hilltop the captain took out his compass and studied his position. 'This is it,' he roared. 'Aye, lads, this is the place old Billy Bones marked on his map. Now down with the chest.' The captain's right hand pushed back his greatcoat. Two loaded pistols gleamed in the strong sun. Slowly his hand drew out . . . a great key. He unlocked the chest and threw open the lid.

Then he reached in and brought out muffins, scones, buttered toast and hot flasks of tea.

'Help yourselves, my hearties,' Captain Kiddo sang out. 'Old Billy Bones certainly knew the best spot for a nice cup of tea.'

Susie's fancy dress

Susie was going to a fancy dress party as a fairy. She had a frilly net dress, a pair of wings and a wand with a star.

Chummy, a friendly spotted dog, saw Susie's wand. Now, Susie often threw sticks for Chummy to fetch, so Chummy jumped up at her, leaving muddy paw-marks on her dress, snatched the wand and ran off with it.

'No,' cried Susie. 'That's not a stick.'

But Chummy didn't understand. He wriggled under a hedge into a field. Susie followed him, and the prickly hedge tore her dress and ripped off her fairy wings.

By this time, Chummy had vanished, so poor Susie had to go to the party without her wand.

All the other little girls were dressed as fairies, too – but they looked lovely. Susie gazed down sadly at her torn, muddy dress; she had lost her wings too, and her wand.

But Mrs Rose who was giving the party gave Susie a beautiful doll.

'All the other girls came as fairies, but I see you are meant to be Cinderella in her ragged dress,' she smiled. 'So you win the prize.'

Susie could hardly believe it. She knew she had Chummy to thank for her prize.

The note in the bottle

In the middle of an island
In the middle of the sea,
Lived a pretty little girl
As sweet as sweet could be.

But soon she felt so all alone,
She threw a bottle in the sea
And in it wrote a little note . . .
'Will someone come and stay
                    with me?

I'll feed you coconuts and fish
Upon a little coral dish,
I'll give you honey from the bees
And luscious fruit from paw-paw
                    trees.'

One day she saw, to her delight,
A sailing boat come into sight.
It was a boy who'd read her note
Inside the bottle left afloat.

The champion conker

On the topmost twig of a chestnut tree hung a prickly green case. The horse-chestnut inside was the last one on the tree, for the village boys had knocked all the others down.

'I'm safe,' said the solitary chestnut.

'Maybe not,' cawed a rook.

In the playground conker fights had begun, but Billy just watched. The bigger boys had taken all the best conkers.

Walking home he stopped to watch the stream, and a rook flew down.

'Climb the spreading candle tree. Reach the top and wait for me,' he cawed.

Billy was very surprised! 'What's a candle tree?' he asked his dad later.

'Why, a chestnut. Remember the blossom,' said his dad.

Billy was too small to climb the tree but his dad went up on a ladder. He was astonished to see the rook.

'You can't reach me,' chuckled the chestnut, but the rook landed on the twig and bent it towards Billy's dad.

And so Billy got his chestnut. And what a champion conker it turned out to be!

The rook sat on the playground railings cawing with delight as he watched Billy swing the conker on its string and crack all the other conkers in the playground.

A tasty snack

The blue balloon

Busy Bobby blew big bubbles,
Smiling Sara skipped and sang,
Frowning Freda, full of troubles,
Said her blue balloon went BANG!

Busy Bobby said, 'Don't bother.'
Smiling Sara said she'd show
Freda how to get another
Blue balloon for Bob to blow.

Busy Bobby bounced and bounded,
Seeing Sara skip and sing,
Blew a blue balloon all rounded,
Sara tied it up with string.

Freda's frowning now no longer,
She saw Sara skip a mile
To the shop to buy a stronger
Blue balloon to make her smile.

The fruit and vegetable show, was being held in a large tent on the village green, and Nanny and Billy the goats who usually lived on the green, were tied up on the far side. But it wasn't so far that Billy couldn't see what was going on.

'There's some delicious food being carried into that tent,' he said. 'I'm going to bite through these ropes so that we can take a look.'

So he tugged and nibbled until they were both free. Then they quietly slipped through the back of the tent.

What a marvellous show! They had never seen such splendid fruit and juicy vegetables. Billy grabbed an apple, sending the pile toppling over, and Nanny snatched a carrot.

'Stop them!' shouted someone, and the chase was on.

Ladies screamed, children shrieked with excitement, tables overturned, and apples, pears, onions and tomatoes rolled together on the floor.

Nanny and Billy had a wonderful time, helping themselves to whatever they fancied, until they were caught, and led away. 'I've never eaten such lovely food. I wish we could have stayed longer,' said Billy. 'But it was a tasty snack.' 'Mmm,' agreed Nanny, 'a very tasty snack.'

The giant's hat

Bumble the giant looked at himself in the mirror. On his head was an enormous straw hat, with ribbon round it.

'What a ridiculous hat!' he muttered. 'How I hate it.' But he couldn't say much, because his wife Thora had made it, and he didn't want to upset her.

Down in the village he saw Billy Binns making a summer house for his children. 'Look!' said Billy. 'There's only the roof to thatch now.'

Then Bumble had an idea. 'My straw hat would make a splendid roof,' he said. 'It's the right shape, and I think it will be big enough.'

'Oh not your beautiful hat!' said Billy.

'Yes, I'd like you to have it, but please don't tell Thora.'

When Bumble reached home Thora asked, 'Where's your hat?'

'Oh – er – I must have left it somewhere.'

'Well I hope it's not lost. It took ages to make. I can't possibly make another one.'

'Thank goodness for that,' thought Bumble.

Next day, when Thora came home, she was very puzzled. 'Billy's summer house has a most peculiar roof,' she said. 'It reminds me of something, but I can't think what it is.'

Bumble didn't say a word. He only smiled to himself.

The lion that squeaked and the mouse that roared

Lion lived in the jungle. Everyone said what a fine lion he was. That is until he opened his mouth to roar. Then out came *a tiny squeak*. Lion was so ashamed he ran deeper into the jungle.

Mouse lived in a hole in the ground. Everyone liked her until she started to squeak. Then out came *a great roar*. 'Go away!' her friends cried. 'You're too noisy.' Sadly mouse wandered deep into the jungle.

One day she met lion. She jumped with fright and let out a great roar. Lion jumped with surprise and squeaked.

They stared at each other for a long time in amazement.

'You roared like I should,' cried the lion.

'And you squeaked like I should,' cried the mouse.

'We can help each other,' they both cried together.

Then mouse crawled onto lion's head. They marched through the jungle and when they met lion's friends mouse roared. Everyone said what a fine roar he had.

They visited mouse's hole in the ground. Lion lowered his head and squeaked. 'How nice to hear you sound like a mouse,' her friends said. 'Do come back home.'

But mouse shook her head. 'It's best this way,' she said winking at Lion. 'We belong together.'

Boomer Bullfrog

The pond animals were excited. Today was the great Jumping Day. Famous frogs from everywhere were there practising jumps.

Only one stood apart . . . Boomer Bullfrog the Great from Texas, U.S.A. He towered head and shoulders above the other frogs. On his head was a tall cowboy hat and on his feet, high-heeled boots.

Old Croaker Frog announced the rules. 'Jump over the pond to win,' he said. 'It's never been done before.'

Tongue twister

Thirty thirsty sailors
Sipping pop in pint pots
At a seaside shop
And shaking sandy seashells
On saucy seagulls!

The frogs lined up. One by one they jumped. Some made it to the middle of the pond. Two almost reached the other side.

Boomer was the last. He removed his boots but left his hat on. 'Never know what the weather's like up there,' he laughed. He stretched his great legs.

Then he jumped. Up like a rocket he soared. Over the pond he zoomed. Higher and higher he rose. Now he was just a speck. Now he vanished.

The pond animals waited and waited. But Boomer never returned!

Far out at sea a ship's captain reported a strange sight. A big frog in a cowboy hat plopped on deck. It asked the captain where it was. Could that be Boomer the Great from Texas?

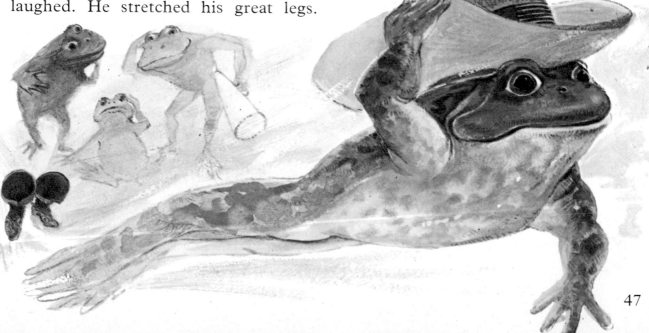

Grandfather's green fingers

'My grandfather has green fingers,' said Jilly, Jane's play-school friend. Jane was astonished. She had never seen anyone with green fingers.

Once, Jilly's grandfather came to fetch her from school, but it was a cold day and he wore gloves, so Jane couldn't see those strange green fingers.

Then, one spring day, Jilly invited Jane to tea with her and her grandfather. Jane was excited. Grandfather wouldn't wear his gloves indoors. Now, she'd see those green fingers.

Jane hurried into the living-room. There was Jilly's grandfather. Jane looked at his hands. 'Oh!' she cried. 'Jilly said you had green fingers, but your fingers aren't green at all.'

Jilly's grandfather chuckled. 'When Jilly said I had green fingers she meant I was a jolly good gardener, my dear.'

'Ohhh!' sighed Jane. 'Is that all?' Jilly's grandfather took Jane into the garden where daffodils bloomed like a sea of yellow waves.

'I hope you're not too disappointed,' he smiled.

'No,' Jane smiled back. 'I expect it would feel very odd if you really did have green fingers.' And Grandfather picked a big bunch of daffodils for Jane to take home.

Claude catches a rat

Claude's sister Celestine was a clever cat. One day, quite bravely, she caught a rat! She went into the kitchen and there it was – the biggest rascal of a rat that she had ever seen. Celestine fluffed up her coat to look fierce, and yowled as loudly as she could. Mrs Plum came running to see what the noise was about. When she saw the rat she seized her broom with a shout and chased it out of the house!

'You good little kitten,' she said to Celestine, and gave her some milk as a reward.

The very next week it was wet. The kittens stayed indoors and played hide-and-seek, and Claude hid in a hat which he found in the hall. He was just tucking in his toes and his nose when he saw something sitting by a box on the table. It was a rat, but it was a very strange round rat – ginger and white with big brown eyes, small pink paws, a nice face, and no tail!

Claude couldn't climb up the table leg because it was polished and slippery, but he decided to surprise the rat and scramble up the table cloth instead. Up he sprang and caught the cloth. He clambered and clung, struggled and swung and all at once his claws got caught, the cloth slipped and the rat squeaked and tumbled off the table, with Claude and the cloth in a tangle on top of it. There was a loud crash! And then a 'SMASH' and a vase of flowers fell too, spilling water over the floor.

Just then Mrs Plum rushed in. How she laughed! For there was a very wet Claude and a very wet guinea pig sitting in a puddle, surrounded by flowers.

A very happy frog

Oh, once there was
A bright green frog
Inside a muddy
Kind of bog.
He lived on flies
And little bugs,

And squidged about
In slimy mud,
Or sat quite quietly
On a log.
He was
a very happy
frog.

The tortoise who lost his shell

A tortoise was eating a lettuce leaf in a field, when he heard a growl.

'Who is eating all my best lettuces?' a voice said.

Tortoise looked up and saw an ugly old troll. 'Please, Sir, I was hungry.'

'Hungery-bungery, you are a thief even to nibble the tiniest leaf.'

'Greenery-beanery, you are a mean-erie to begrudge me a bit of lettuce,' said Tortoise.

'For those words,' said Troll, 'you shall pay. Shell, shell, off with you.'

And before Tortoise could say *wind-in-the-clover*, off flew his shell.

'Hohoho,' laughed the Troll.

'Ohohoh,' moaned Tortoise, and began crawling away, very shivery and frightened. He hid in a wood and cried big, cold tears. Suddenly he heard two voices. He looked round to see a raven looking down at him and a hedgehog looking up at him.

'Why do you cry?' they asked. He wiped away his tears with his claw and, between big sobs, he told them his story.

'Tell you what I'll do,' said Raven, 'I'll fly to the lettuce field, find your shell and bring it back to you.'

'And I'll stitch it on with one of my needles,' said Hedgehog.

And soon Tortoise was as neat and smart as he had ever been.

The lost ball

In a house not far from ours lived a dog named Fred. One day he lost his favourite blue ball. He searched everywhere for it – under the bed, behind the chair, inside the cupboard. But he couldn't find it.

Fred went to look in the garden. The ginger cat was sitting on the wall.

'Ginger cat, do you know where my blue ball is?' asked Fred.

'Miaow, no,' said the cat. 'Ask the hens.'

So Fred ran to the shed. 'Hens, have you seen my blue ball?'

'Cluck, no,' said the hens. 'Ask the owl. He'll know.'

So Fred went in search of the owl. 'Please, have you seen my blue ball?' he asked.

'Whoo-oo-oo,' said the wise owl. 'Ask your master. He knows.'

Fred ran back to the house to find his master. 'Wuff-wuff,' he barked.

'What's the matter, Fred?' asked the little boy. 'Have you lost your ball?'

'*Wuff!*' barked Fred.

'It's in your basket,' said the little boy. 'You put it there this morning.'

Then Fred remembered. He had hidden his blue ball under the cushion. Why? So he would know where it was when he wanted to play. Silly old Fred!

Melons and acorns

Once long ago in faraway Persia a farmer was gathering melons, but the harvest had been poor and the melons were few.

Overhead was an oak tree on which a million billion trillion acorns were growing, hanging on every branch.

'Oh,' sighed the farmer, 'I wish I could understand why the Good Lord allows so many acorns to grow on one tree, and so few melons to flourish on the ground. Why don't melons grow on this tree instead of acorns? So much more sensible.'

At that very moment a brown squirrel knocked against an acorn, which fell from the tree and hit the old farmer right in the middle of his big, bald head.

'Oh, oh!' cried the farmer, rubbing the sore spot where the acorn had hit him. 'Now I understand. The Good Lord knows better than I. If this tree had grown big melons instead of tiny acorns I should now have a broken head.'

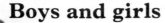

The bored lion

'Oh, that lion,' cried the animals in the zoo, 'he never stops grumbling.'

'But I'm so B-O-R-E-D,' roared the lion.

'Well,' said the tiger, 'what do people do when they're bored?'

'They paint pictures and arrange flowers, and things like that,' said the bear.

'Then bring me some flowers,' wailed the lion.

So every morning the animals brought fresh flowers to the lion's cage, and he spent the whole day arranging them.

When visitors came to the zoo they all stopped at the lion's cage.

'How beautiful!' they said.

'What a clever lion!'

'Fancy that!'

The lion paced up and down amongst the flowers feeling quite giddy with pride. And when the visitors had gone he made up stories about himself, and told the other animals what a wonderful lion he was, and how there had never been such a clever lion as he.

'Oh, that lion,' cried the animals in the zoo. 'He never stops showing off!'

The night watchman

Timothy shivered beneath the warm bedclothes. He hated the dark and the howl of wind down the chimney. Hail stones bounced off the window pane, and trees in the garden swayed and rustled in the night.

Timothy was unhappy. He had lost his present from Grandad – a yellow kite which had blown away in the strong wind. Two big tears rolled down his cheeks.

A gentle tap came from the window. 'What was that?' said Timothy. He sat up in bed and looked round the room. No-one was there, but he heard a soft voice singing:

'I am the watchman of the night
I'll keep you safe 'til morning light.'

A little elf dressed in green peeped through the window. He carried a bright lantern. 'Don't cry, Timothy,' he called. 'I am the night watchman. I look after all little boys and girls. All will be well, wait and see.' Then the elf turned and flew off into the night.

When Timothy awoke the next morning, there on the bed, lay his new yellow kite!

Carry, the carrying dog

Jane's dog, Carry, loved to carry things – sticks, stones, bones, rubber balls, newspapers, but especially shoes. Nobody ever knew where their shoes were, because Carry was always taking them from one room to another.

Once, she took Jane's favourite doll, and left it in the garden. Jane was very angry, and Carry went and hid under the kitchen table.

Next day, Jane and her mother, and Carry, went to the park. Jane put her doll down on a bench, while she went on the swings.

When they got home, Jane said suddenly: 'I've lost my doll. It's that wicked Carry – she's taken my doll again.'

Carry ran off, and Jane cried and cried, because she thought Carry had taken her doll and lost it in the park.

Then they heard a scratching at the door, and there was Carry, holding the doll gently in her mouth. She'd gone back and fetched it from the park bench where Jane had left it.

Jane hugged her and said, 'Oh, thank you, Carry – I'll never be angry with you again.'

Statues

The Old Woman who lived in a shoe had so many children she didn't know what to do. Kind Goldilocks said she'd mind the children while the Old Woman went shopping.

What imps those children were! They slid down the stairs on tin trays; they swung on the curtains and pulled them down; and they were SO noisy! Then, Goldilocks had an idea.

'Let's play a game,' she cried.

The children loved games, so they listened to Goldilocks.

'Hop, skip and jump about,' she said. 'And when I shout "Stop!" you must stand quite still, like statues. The child who stands still for the longest time shall have a lovely iced cake.'

The children were excited. Each wanted to win the cake. So, when Goldilocks cried, 'STOP!' they stood absolutely still—some on tiptoe, some on one foot. And it was so quiet you could hear a mouse sneeze.

When the Old Woman came home, she was astonished. 'It's a game,' whispered Goldilocks. 'The child who moves last wins an iced cake.' She handed the Old Woman the iced cake and slipped away.

She'll certainly never look after those naughty children again!

Nuts

Three topmost squirrels, Wug, Wig
and Wag,
Lived in the topmost tree
In the topmost wood on the topmost hill,
Within easy reach of the sea.

Wug, Wig and Wag had sharp
bright eyes
And teeth that were white and strong;
Their long bushy tails waved in rhythm
To the beat of their favourite song.

'Hazel-nut, cob-nut, almond, brazil
And walnut we've never refused,
But if you offer us prickly chestnuts,
We confess we are not amused!'

Baby Rupert and the snowballs

When the Rabbits woke up, the fields were white and glistening. It had snowed!

Rosie and Ronald couldn't wait to go out and play.

'Can we take Rupert?' asked Rosie.

'No,' said Mrs Rabbit, 'Baby Rupert is much too small.'

Rosie and Ronald had a lovely game, slipping and sliding and falling head over heels in the cold snow.

'I wish Rupert could play in the snow,' said Rosie.

'We could take him some snowballs,' said Ronald. 'He'd like that.'

But when they went indoors, their arms full of snowballs, Rupert was fast asleep. So they put the snowballs by his bed and raced out again.

Mrs Rabbit went upstairs later to fetch Rupert for dinner.

'Oh, my goodness,' she cried. 'Where has all this water come from?'

Rosie and Ronald rushed upstairs to see Rupert splashing happily in a puddle by his bed. The snowballs had melted!

'Oh,' said Rosie and Ronald, and told Mrs Rabbit what they had done.

Mrs Rabbit laughed. 'So Rupert played in the snow, after all,' she said.

The clean sweep

'The chimney-sweep's coming today,' said Pam to Peter.

The chimney-sweep had a white van. He wore white overalls and he spread white sheets round the fireplace. He used a special big vacuum cleaner with round bristly brushes which reached to the top of the chimney.

'Go outside and see if the brush is sticking out of the chimney,' he said.

Pam and Peter went outside and saw the brush popping up from the chimney.

'I liked that,' said Peter. 'Let's play with our vacuum cleaner and pretend to be chimney-sweeps.'

'It's only for carpets and things,' said Pam as Peter took out the cleaner.

Then Peter got Dad's long fishing rod and he tied Mum's pan scrub on the end and poked it along the vacuum tube.

But the pan scrub got stuck. 'Dad's fishing rod is for FISHING, not chimney-sweeping,' said Pam.

'That's strange . . .' said Mum when she switched on the cleaner, 'it's growling. Something's stuck in the tube.'

It took ages to get the pan scrub out.

'How on earth did *that* get in there?' said Mum.

'I think proper sweeps are best, after all,' said Peter, as he and Pam ran off to play.

The little house

Once upon a time there was a little house. It stood all alone on the edge of a wood, and no-one had lived there for a long, long time.

It was a very sad little house. Its windows were dirty, and its floors were covered with dust.

'How lonely I am,' sighed the little house. 'Nobody wants to live in me.'

But one day some workmen came along. They began to hammer and bang inside the little house until it shook all over. They cleaned the windows and swept the floors, and pulled up all the weeds in the garden.

The next day a big van arrived. It had furniture for the rooms, and carpets for the floors, and curtains for the windows, and pictures for the walls.

The day after that, two children came with their mother and father. They ran up and down the stairs, and looked inside all the rooms, and played outside in the garden.

'Isn't it a *beautiful* house!' they told one another. 'We're going to be so happy living here!'

And the little house smiled, because it knew it would never be lonely ever again.

The magic carpet

Queen Zoza was so proud that she always made people put down a red carpet for her to walk on. And anyone who didn't cheer her, was punished. Nobody liked her.

Her frightened subjects asked a magician to help them, and when the Queen stepped from her carriage on to the red carpet, he chanted a secret spell.

As Queen Zoza walked, the carpet got longer in front of her. She went on walking, with her nose in the air, not noticing that the carpet was leading her through the crowds and out of the town.

It got longer and longer, and Queen Zoza walked on and on, across fields and over hills and through forests.

The magic carpet went on and on, and came to a cliff. The Queen, with her nose in the air, didn't see it, and walked over the edge. Down, down she fell, and disappeared with a *plop* into the sea, leaving her crown floating on the water.

Then the people really cheered. They made the magician their King – and used the enormous carpet for bicycle races.

Agatha the rag doll

Agatha the rag doll had been bought at a jumble sale. She sat in the toy cupboard looking rather sad.

'Shall I ask her if she'd like some chocolate cake?' whispered Edward Bear.

'It's a little early for cake,' smiled Wendy the doll.

'I know,' roared Elephant, 'how about a nice hot bath?'

'Oh yes, please,' said Agatha.

There was a moment's silence then they all burst out laughing. Elephant rushed off and filled the tub. Jolly fetched a towel. Pussycat brought out her perfumed soap, and Agatha was soon in the bathtub.

While Wendy washed her hair, Pussycat scrubbed her back. Then they wrapped her in the big warm towel. Agatha brushed out her hair and made two long blonde pigtails. Wendy lent her a pretty spotted dress and pussycat found her a clean apron.

'Oh thank you,' said Agatha, 'I feel so much better now.' They went to join the other toys.

'Wow,' said Elephant, blushing to the very tip of his trunk. 'Would you care to join us Your Majesty,' said Edward Bear making a deep bow.

'I would indeed,' smiled Agatha, and laughing happily they all sat down to a delicious, if rather late breakfast.

How many eyes?

Six large hippos in a pool,
Keeping wet and very cool.
Count their sleepy little eyes
Winking at the dragon-flies.

Ten striped tigers crouching low
Where the grass waves to and fro
Count the amber eyes that stare
When we pass all unaware.

Twelve long pythons gently glide
Through the jungle where they hide
Count their emerald eyes and see
Them coil and twine around each tree.

Black-eyed Susan

Grandpa had a greenhouse and Tommy loved visiting him and helping him in it. It was Tommy's job to keep the flower-pots tidy, Grandpa said. But sometimes he would let Tommy sow some seeds in boxes.

On his next visit Tommy jumped up and down in excitement, for his seeds were all shooting up madly over the top of the box. Tommy wondered what the plants would be like when they were fully grown.

Grandpa said, 'Wait and see. These are best of all – they're called Black-eyed Susan.'

Tommy laughed for his mother's name was Susan. 'But Grandpa,' he said, 'flowers don't have eyes.'

'Well this one does,' said Grandpa. 'You'll see.'

The seedlings grew taller, and Grandpa put sticks beside them to support them. He gave two pots to Tommy to take home. 'Now you begin to watch them Tommy,' he said. 'Don't forget to water them, and look at them before you go to school each day.'

So Tommy did, and one day there appeared two yellow flowers – and in the centre of them were little black circles.

Tommy understood then what Grandpa had meant. 'They *are* like Mummy's eyes,' he laughed.

Peter and Jolly again

Peter's friend was a carthorse called Jolly. Each day, he went to see him, and take him something to eat, usually dandelion leaves.

The enormous horse would keep a look-out for Peter, and gallop across the field to greet him. This time, Peter fed him a carrot, and put his arms around the long neck which reached down to him.

Then he climbed the gate, and stroked him and talked to him. The huge, broad back suddenly looked very inviting. Dare he?

Gingerly, Peter slid onto Jolly's back. The horse looked round in surprise. 'Come on Jolly!' said Peter. 'Will you take me for a ride?'

Jolly tossed his head and walked, with Peter holding his mane. Peter was thrilled.

Then, he heard voices. There at the gate were his friends, clapping and cheering. Jolly walked up to them.

'Oh Peter,' cried his friends, '*do* let us have a ride, too.'

Peter was unsure. But he needn't have worried. Jolly took them all for a gentle walk around the field, stopping at the gate for each one to get off.

Peter was proud of him. 'You are the best friend ever,' he told him.

Peter piglet learns to swim

'Don't get your pink coat dirty today,' warned Mummy Pig.

Peter Piglet wandered down to the river bank. He didn't know what to do. Usually he wallowed in the mud, rolling over and sliding, but he knew Mummy would be cross if he got dirty.

Just then Peter stumbled over a stone and did a somersault right into the mud.

A mouse in the house
(A finger rhyme)

One little mouse sat alone on the stairs;
Two little mice ran under the chair.
Three little mice in the larder hid,
Found the jam pot, lifted the lid.
Four little mice at the table sat,
Eating cornflakes until they were fat.
Five little mice all jumped into bed,
Pulled the covers right over their heads.
Six little mice, chased by a broom,
Skipped and danced all over the room.
Seven little mice, each with a high squeak,
Sang a new song every day of the week.
Eight little mice warmed their toes by the fire,
Watching the flames go higher and higher.
Nine little mice each wore a funny hat
Ten little mice ran away from the cat!

(Hide all your fingers behind your back.)

He was covered in it from the tip of his snout to the end of his curly tail!

'Whatever will Mummy say!' he exclaimed.

Freddie Frog poked his head out of the river.

'Come for a swim after you've finished playing,' he said. 'You will soon be clean again.'

'I can't swim,' wailed Peter.

'I'll teach you,' said Freddie. 'You shouldn't play near water if you can't swim.'

So Freddie Frog showed Peter how to swim.

'That was almost as much fun as playing in the mud,' said Peter, drying himself in the sun on the grassy bank. 'I think I shall have a swim after mud-playing everyday.'

Mummy Pig was pleased too.

Sonny the dolphin

Sonny the dolphin lived in a pool at the end of the pier with two other dolphins.

In the summer, the children came. They played on the sands and paddled, but best of all they loved watching the dolphins do their tricks.

One day Sonny was naughty. He leapt high in the air – S-P-L-A-S-H – and landed amongst the sealions who were waiting for their dinner.

'You aren't having any of our fish,' grunted one.

'There's no room for you here,' honked another.

So Sonny leapt into the sea. It was great fun!

Then a storm came and poor Sonny wished he hadn't left his pool. He hid under the pier until the sun shone again.

OOMPAH, OOMPAH! came the noise of a big bass drum. Sonny could see people watching a brass band on the pier but they didn't notice when little Mark, fishing from the pier, fell into the water.

'Climb on me,' said Sonny, and swam towards the beach with Mark on his back.

Sonny was soon back in his pool and happy to be there, but he was rather proud of his adventure. He had a special friend now – Mark, who brought him fish every day.

The Robins' warm nest

'What are we going to line the nest with this year?' asked Mrs Robin. 'Soon I'll be laying my eggs and I don't want them to hatch before it's really warm enough for the fledglings.'

The days did begin to get a little warmer but the robins still needed a warm lining for the nest.

Close by their nest stood a house where there lived an old lady. The robins heard her say to herself one day, 'I'm so glad the sun is shining today.' They wondered why, and then they saw her carrying out a chair and sit outside with a large cushion on her knee.

'My dear,' said Mr Robin, 'I do believe you will get your warm nest.'

Three television sets

Three television sets
Went to the zoo,
An elephant sat on one
And then there were
Two television sets
Waiting in the sun,
One got overheated
And then there was
One television set
All on its own,
I went and bought it
And now it's at home!

The old lady unpicked the end of the cushion and shook all the feathers into a new cover. A gust of wind lifted the cover up and a handful of feathers flew out. The old lady let them go, for she had more than enough.

So Mr and Mrs Robin flew down and gathered up as many as they could to line their nest and make it warm for the fledglings.

The squeaky lion

A great lion opened his mouth to speak
But, instead of a roar – out came a
*   squeak!*
Down from the trees swung a monkey
*   bold.*
He said, 'How odd! Have you a cold?'
'No!' squeaked the lion, 'But all that
*   roaring*
Really does become boring,
So just for a change it's rather nice
To make a different sound – like mice.'

Inch Elf and Oliver Otter

Inch Elf loved his brightly painted toadstool, and every day he polished it until it shone like gold.

The ladder that Oliver Otter had made for him leant against the toadstool, so that Inch could climb up and down.

One day, Inch was sitting on his toadstool repairing his old hat. The sun was very hot.

'I need a new hat,' said Inch, to himself. 'The sun is burning my head.' And he climbed down the ladder and sat under a buttercup. 'It's much cooler down here,' he said.

Inch hadn't noticed how hot the sun was when he lived on the river. The beautiful waterlily petals had shaded him then.

Inch went down to the river bank to find Oliver Otter. 'He is such a clever fellow. I'm sure he can make the sun stop shining on my toadstool.'

Oliver Otter laughed when Inch asked him to move the sun.

'I can make you a shade for your toadstool,' said Oliver Otter, and he put a tiny hole in the top of the toadstool, then stood a pretty daisy umbrella in it.

Inch climbed up the ladder and sat under his sunshade. 'Oh, thank you Oliver' he said. 'You are clever.'

The star that disappeared

There was once a little girl named Nicola. And every night at bedtime she would look through her window to say goodnight to her favourite star. It shone very brightly in the sky and seemed to twinkle at her over the rooftops.

But one night when Nicola looked out, the star had disappeared!

'Where have you gone?' she called out. 'Please come back, the sky is so dark without your light.'

The wind was blowing past Nicola's window, and he heard her. He decided to help. He rushed away, over the rooftops and up into the sky until he came to the place where the star usually shone.

And the wind saw what had happened. A big cloud had wrapped itself around Nicola's star and put out its light. So the wind began to puff, harder and harder. And the big cloud was blown far away into the dark sky, and the star was able to shine again.

When Nicola looked out of her window once more, there was her favourite star twinkling down at her as it always did.

'Goodnight, star,' she called happily.

Rumblestart the tractor

Rumblestart was a new, red tractor, but before long, he became quite tired of going up and down a field all day.

'How I wish,' he said to the two old tractors in the field beside him, 'that I could travel wherever I liked!'

The two old tractors just smiled at each other.

That night the moon came out and Rumblestart decided to go. He started himself up and set off. 'Freedom at last!' he sang, and chugged happily along.

Suddenly, lights dazzled him, and a huge lorry thundered past, giving him a good shake.

Next, a motor-bike, came hurtling straight towards him – and only just missed him!

Cars hooted and made him jump, and a round part in the road sent him quite dizzy.

Back he chugged, longing for the quiet of his field. He was so thirsty for some petrol, he was frightened he wouldn't get there. He just managed it!

And one old tractor gave the other old tractor, a big long wink.

Jenny's special friend

Jenny woke up feeling sad. Today was Mummy's birthday and she didn't have a present to give her. She put on her warm coat and crept out into the field. In a tree there, Jenny had a very special friend – a Tree Fairy. This was a secret because she didn't think that grown-ups really believed in fairies. But Jenny did, because the Tree Fairy was her very own and could do wonderful things.

She called very softly up into the branches, and almost at once she heard the whispering of fairy wings as a little creature, no bigger than a butterfly, came fluttering lightly down beside her.

The Tree Fairy listened while Jenny told her how much she would like to give her Mummy a present, then she flew away into the branches.

Jenny slowly wandered back through the field. Suddenly, she stopped. Right in front of her was a bright red poppy . . . then big yellow daisies and purple bells.

It's all very odd

What animal is on your head?
What tree upon your hand?
What kind of pet is never fed
Though on it you may stand?

What thing has ears but cannot hear?
What eyes but cannot see?
What has a tongue but says, I fear,
No word to you or me?

The field was filled with flowers!
Jenny's mother could hardly believe it. 'It's just like fairyland,' she said. 'Happy birthday, Mummy,' said Jenny.

Tumbledown and the Wizard

Tumbledown was an elf who was always falling over. At the elves' picnic he fell over, upsetting the lemonade. When he went shopping he fell over, breaking the eggs. He fell over at the seaside – right into the water – and came home soaking wet.

Tumbledown went to see Willy Wizard.

'Can you help me?' he asked.

Willy gave him some magic cream, but that didn't help at all.

So Willy Wizard gave him a big spoonful of his Very Special Medicine, but that only made Tumbledown stand on his head.

'Oh dear, oh dear,' said Willy, as he stood the Elf the right way up.

Then he had an idea. 'Have you tried looking where you're going?'

'I don't think so,' said Tumbledown.

'Try,' said Willy Wizard.

Tumbledown did.

And do you know? He hardly ever falls over now.

Daffodil makes a quick recovery

When Tom heard a loud quacking in the farmyard, he left his breakfast and ran outside to see what was wrong.

'Look Mum,' he said, coming back inside with a little duckling cradled in his hands. 'Daffodil's sick. Mother Duck was trying to tell us.'

Poor Daffodil had been swimming and had caught a chill. 'What can we do?' said Tom, holding the weak, shivering little bird.

His Mum had an idea. 'We'll make a soft bed for her in a cardboard box, with a hot-water bottle to keep her warm.'

'You're a lucky duckling having a bed like this,' smiled Tom, as he put Daffodil into the box.

At first Daffodil could only reply with a feeble little cheep, but in a few minutes she was sitting up as bright as ever.

'I knew she'd make a quick recovery,' said Tom to his Mum as they watched Daffodil scamper back to Mother Duck. 'You can't keep that little duckling away from her breakfast for long.'

Sarah-Jane learns to swim

Sarah-Jane was on holiday with her school-friends. They could swim, but Sarah-Jane couldn't. She sat alone on the sands, picked up a seashell and held it to her ear, expecting to hear the sea sound.

Instead, she heard a voice: 'Come to the Big Grey Rock, Sarah-Jane'.

Still holding the seashell, Sarah-Jane did as the voice bid. Behind the Big Grey Rock sat two mermaids combing their hair with pearl and coral combs. One had long green hair, and the other blue hair.

'Hello,' said the mermaids to Sarah-Jane. 'You got our message then?'

'Hello. And yes', said Sarah-Jane.

'Come for a swim?' they invited.

'I c-c-can't swim,' Sarah-Jane sadly confessed.

'Can't swim? Don't be silly,' said the mermaids. 'We'll teach you.'

They took her hands in theirs and then Sarah-Jane found herself swimming between them. It was wonderful, and so easy. Finally, the mermaids disappeared into the deep sea, but Sarah-Jane went on swimming.

'I thought you couldn't swim,' Sarah-Jane's best friend, Emma, called to her. 'Who taught you?'

'You'd never, never, *never* guess,' Sarah-Jane replied.

Why?

Why should a ladder go up?
Why should a snake descend?
Why should noughts battle with crosses?
Why should a full-back defend?
Why should a rook be a castle?
Why should a draught be huffed?
Why should a thimble be hunted?
Why should a blind man be buffed?
Why should a tiddly wink?
Why is a meeting a rally?
Why does a huntsman wear pink?
Why call a marble an alley?

No one has answered correctly
More than half of our questions, I fear,
So if you have got seven or more right,
You're our Reader of the Year!

The spinning signpost

Everything was mixed up at the busy cross-roads. Car drivers didn't know which way to turn. Cyclists were confused. Lorry drivers scratched their heads . . . and all because the signpost there didn't know which way to point!

First it pointed to town down one of the roads. The cars, lorries and cyclists headed that way.

Then the signpost swung about and pointed across the fields. 'Bumpety, bump,' went the cars, lorries and cycles as they sped over the rough ground.

'I say,' one of the drivers shouted, looking back, 'now it's pointing the way we came!'

Soon a farmer came by on his tractor. He looked at the puzzled people. Then he looked at the spinning signpost. 'Town is down that way,' he pointed, 'and I know where that signpost belongs.'

The people drove off happily.

And the signpost? Now it sits happily on top of the farmer's barn.

It was really a weathervane, you see.

Buster Bassett and the bedspread

'I'll fetch the milk,' said Buster Bassett. He tripped over his long ears and crashed into the bottles, knocking them down.

'You silly dog,' scolded Miss Catrina Cat. She was spring cleaning. Buster went for a long walk by the river.

Miss Catrina was having a nap when he returned. Buster was tired too and he climbed onto his bed. Too late he remembered he was still wearing his boots. There was mud all over his pretty bedspread.

'I must wash it before Catrina wakes,' he thought. So he scrubbed it clean and hung it on the hedge.

When it was dry, Buster started to bring it in. He gave it a pull but it was stuck on the hedge. He pulled harder and it came away but with a loud tearing sound. The bedspread was torn in two!

Catrina came into the garden.

'Just what I need for my curtains,' she cried. 'I can hem the sides and they'll be ready to hang.'

Buster was pleased that Catrina wasn't cross.

'I have a blanket that would be much nicer for your bed,' she said.

Teddy's wash

Poor dirty Teddy
Lying on the floor,
We put him in the washer
With the round glass door.

Poor soapy Teddy,
The water rushed in,
The washer let it out again
And put him in a spin.

The dryer fluffed him into shape,
And when he was ready,
We took him out and then I had
The hottest, cleanest Teddy!

The Sand Witches

There were once three little witches who lived beside the sea. They were called the Sand Witches, and they swept the sands to keep them smooth and tidy.

The Sand Witches made their home in a little cave among the seaweed. But one day a naughty boy came to the seaside. He pulled down the seaweed, and he filled the cave full of pebbles and broken shells.

The three little witches were very angry. 'Where shall we live now?' they said. And while the boy was eating his picnic lunch, they blew sand into his icecream and his orange juice, to punish him for his naughtiness.

The next day another boy came to the seaside. It was his birthday, and he had a new bucket and spade. He began to build a big sandcastle. It had a door and windows, and shells on the walls, and a flag fluttering on top.

When he had finished building, the boy said to himself, 'I wish there was someone to live in my castle.'

The Sand Witches heard him. 'We will come to live in your beautiful sand-castle,' they said. And as far as I know, they live there still.

The bravest dog in the world

Just down the road, there used to live a dog named Percy. He considered himself to be the bravest dog in the world.

One day Percy's master went out, and told him to guard the house. Percy was very pleased. 'I hope a burglar comes along,' he thought, 'then I can bark and frighten him away, and everyone will know how brave I am.'

Just then there came a loud noise. *Bang! Bang!* it went. Percy looked round. But there was nothing there.

'Perhaps it's the burglar trying to break into my house,' he growled.

Then the noise came again, even louder. *Bang! Bang!* It was right behind him. But when Percy jumped round, there was still nothing there. He began to feel a bit frightened. Whatever could it be?

Soon Percy's master came home. The dog was very glad to see him. But as he was saying hello, the noise came louder than ever. *Bang! Bang! Bang!*

Percy's master laughed. 'What a noise your tail makes!' he said. 'Every time it wags, it bumps against the door.'

'So that's what it was,' thought Percy. 'Fancy being frightened of my own tail. I'm not so brave after all.'

Alexander's toffee papers

Once there was a bag of toffees in Alexander's house but they didn't last long because all the family liked them. Alexander's particular favourites were the chocolate ones that tasted of peppermint in the middle.

'Don't forget to save the toffee papers,' said his grandpa.

'Why?' asked Alexander.

'I'll tell you when you have a pocketful,' said Grandpa.

Alexander ran round the house and collected every toffee paper he could find and soon his jersey pocket sounded rustly as he moved.

'I've got a pocketful now,' he said.

'Well,' explained Grandpa, 'if you smooth out the ones made of see-through paper you can pretend they are little coloured windows. Hold them up in front of your eyes and see what happens!'

Grandpa was quite right about those toffee papers. They were just like little windows and in such lovely colours . . . reds, yellows, greens, even dark blues. Looking outside through green papers turned the garden into a seaweedy, underwater place. Red papers made everywhere warm and glowing, and dark blue papers made bright mornings seem like bedtime! Yellow papers were Alexander's favourites, especially on dull days when there was nothing nice to do. They changed dull days into days full of golden sunshine.

The little pink house

The little pink house smiled under its thatched roof. The two front windows twinkled. The little brass knocker sniffed the pretty flowers, and the polished letter-box grinned. The birds sang, and the sun beamed.

An old man stopped at the gate, and smiled at the little pink house.

Then a big, black cloud came and blotted out the sun.

'Everyone smiles when they see the little pink house, but they only scowl at me,' said the cloud angrily. So he made it rain.

The little pink house got very wet. The roof dripped, the knocker and the letter-box lost their shine and the walls were dark and ugly. The flowers hung their heads and cried. A man hurried by, then a woman under a red umbrella. Children, out from school, ran past. Even the birds deserted the little pink house.

When the big, black cloud saw this, it laughed. It laughed so hard that it rolled right out of sight!

The sun came out. It shone on the little pink house. The roof steamed, the letter-box gleamed and the walls turned pink again. The flowers stopped crying, and the birds flew back to the garden.

A man stopped at the gate and smiled, and the little pink house smiled back.

The lost bone

There was once a little boy called Mark. One day, he heard his puppy crying. 'What's the matter, Spot?' he asked.

'I've lost the bone I had yesterday,' said Spot.

Mark and Spot went into the garden to look for the bone. Ginger, the cat from next-door, was sitting by the rubbish heap and she was cross when she saw them. 'Go away, can't you see I'm watching for mice?'

'Have you seen Spot's bone?' asked Mark.

'No I haven't,' Ginger answered. 'I don't like bones.'

Rufus, the big dog from across the road was eating a bone. 'Are you eating Spot's bone?' asked Mark.

'No, I'm not,' said Rufus. 'I dug it up from my garden.'

'Do you think you could have buried your bone, Spot?' asked Mark.

'I can't remember,' Spot replied sadly.

Just then, Mother called, 'Time to go shopping.' So Mark put on Spot's lead and they went with Mummy to the shops.

At the butcher's they bought Spot another bone. When they got home Mark said, 'Go to bed, Spot, and have a rest.'

Spot jumped into his basket, landed on a hard knobbly lump and called to Mark, 'Look, I've found my bone!'

Mummy laughed, 'He's a clever puppy – now he has two bones.'

Super-market

Our town has a huge super-market;
My mum took me there yesterday.
She gave me my own special basket –
I could buy what I liked; she would pay.

I began with a small bag of peanuts,
Then I popped in a chocolate cigar,
A packet of liquorice all-sorts,
Some mints and a giant candy bar.

I took biscuits all chocolate-coated
From the counter a bit further on;
There were cakes but the ones with the cream in,
I am sorry to say, had all gone.

My mum paid the bill as she'd promised,
And smiled as if nothing was wrong,
But next time she goes shopping, I reckon
She's not likely to take me along.

A day out

The hard round pebbles hurt my feet,
The candy rock's too hard to eat,
The frisky breeze blows hats away,
The sun's too hot for me to play.

My lolly melts and leaves its stick
Before I have a chance to lick.
But, oh, what fun it is to be
Up to my middle in cool, blue sea!

A town called Ditherington

There was once a small town called Ditherington which was built high on a hill-top, far, far away. It wasn't very smart, but it was home to the people who lived there.

One day, something very odd began to happen. Breakfast eggs began to pop out of their egg cups – then the trees and houses began to dither and shake – and the people decided to leave the town. They all started to run at once and everyone left Ditherington in a mad, helter-skelter rush for the bottom of the hill and the woods beyond.

All, that is, except one small, curious boy called Richard. He sat himself down on a rock at the bottom of the hill and waited.

It was worth waiting for, because

instead of falling down like everyone had said it would, Ditherington began to go up, up, up, high into the sky – and from underneath the hill, a long neck and four legs appeared.

It was a dinosaur!

A huge, enormous, gigantic, dozey-looking dinosaur!

The dinosaur blinked sleepily and peered down at Richard.

'Hello, small creature,' he said.

'I'm *not* small,' said Richard, 'it's you that's big!' But the dinosaur wasn't listening. He wasn't doing anything much except looking around. Then he took one great step with each of his four great feet, and yawned an enormous yawn.

'I'm so *tired*,' he said. 'I'm always tired. I suppose that's why I'm called Dozey.'

'You've got our town on your back,' said Richard. 'You must have been asleep a long time.' But the dozey dinosaur wasn't listening. His eyes were shut. He tucked in his neck and legs and went back to sleep.

When all was quiet once more, the people of the town came out of the woods and found Richard still staring at the hill. When he told them all what had been happening, they didn't believe him.

'Silly boy, he dreamt it all!' they said.

But Richard knew he hadn't. Besides, nobody could ever quite explain why the hill had moved a bit to one side or why

there were four big holes that looked just like footprints at the bottom of the hill! Nobody, that is, except one small, curious boy called Richard.

The window cleaners

'Look at those men cleaning windows,' said Pam to Peter when they were in town.

'I'd like to clean windows,' said Peter. 'Let's clean Dad's car windows when we get home.'

So they got Mum's washing-up liquid and a sponge, and some water. Then, Peter squirted a big P for Peter on Dad's car door with the washing-up liquid.

'Stop it,' said Pam, and she tipped water over the P for Peter and it all went bubbly and disappeared.

So Peter started to tip water on Pam's car door.

'We are supposed to be *proper* window cleaners, remember,' said Pam.

So Peter got his cloth to wash the window properly, and . . . he found it was OPEN!

'The water would have gone inside the car,' he said, and he shut the window.

When Dad came out, he said, 'I've got a new car.'

'Not new, Dad,' laughed Pam and Peter, 'just clean, that's all.'

Jack Daw's new nest

Once, a long time ago, there was a beautiful bird whose feathers were as white as snow. His name was Jack Daw, and he lived in a nest in a tree.

One chilly winter morning, Jack Daw said to himself, 'It's cold here. I must find somewhere warmer to make my nest.'

He flew about until he came to a chimney on a house roof. And as he rested there, he began to feel nice and warm. He didn't know that down at the bottom of the chimney a fire was burning in the grate.

'This is the place where I shall live,' decided the white bird.

He built his new nest inside the warm chimney, and all that winter he was very cosy indeed.

But gradually his beautiful white feathers began to change colour. They grew darker and darker until they were quite black. Jack Daw didn't mind – he thought black feathers were much more handsome than white ones.

And ever since then, all Jack Daw birds have made their nests in chimneys, and their feathers are as black as soot.

The right time

The nursery clock says six o'clock,
The kitchen clock says eight,
Daddy's watch says seven o'clock;
I hope I won't be late.

Mummy says that one is fast
And one is one hour slow.
One is right but which it is
I really do not know.

Polly the china pig

Old Miss Mary had a pretty china pig called Polly. Early one morning Polly thought she would like to go and see the world.

She called at a farm to make friends with the pigs there. But the pigs didn't like Polly because she was too smart.

'Go away, you're too clean!' they grunted, rolling in the mud, and Polly ran away from them.

She went into a shop with china figures like herself in the window.

'Good morning,' she said politely to a pair of tall elegant china cats.

But the cats didn't like Polly because she wasn't smart enough for them.

'Go away, you're too ordinary,' they said. 'Nobody will want to buy you.' But somebody did!

Old Miss Mary knew exactly which way Polly had gone—because Polly was a money-box pig, and she had dropped a trail of pennies all the way along the road!

Polly was overjoyed when she saw Old Miss Mary come into the shop. She had quite enough pennies to buy Polly back, and Polly was glad her adventure was over.

Bragon-the-Dragon

'Hello, Mum,' said Bragon-the-Dragon, entering the kitchen.

'Hello, Son!' said his mother.

Bragon sniffed at the air. 'What's for dinner?' he asked.

'Cucumber-custard and apple dough-nuts,' she replied.

It was Bragon's favourite dish but today, instead of saying 'Oh GOOD', he said, 'We-e-e-elll, I'm not really very hungry. You see, Mum, I've just eaten four little boys, three little girls and two little pigs . . .'

'Now, Bragon, that's enough,' said Mrs Dragon. 'I do wish you would not tell lies, son. Draw up your chair to the table and eat up your cucumber-custard.'

Bragon obeyed.

After lunch, he thought, 'Huh! I'll show Mum. I'll go and catch a cow and take it home for supper tonight.' So he went to the meadow where the cows and little calves were munching the green grass.

He thought that the cows looked rather big so he decided to take home a baby calf.

He said soothingly to a little brown calf, 'Cushy-cow, cushy-cow, come along with me.'

But the calf's mother heard him. She lowered her horns and said, 'MOOOOO-OOOOOGOOOOOOOOOO.' It was a terrible sound.

Bragon was terrified. He turned tail and ran out of the field as fast and as far as he could go. Then he sat down on an old log until he felt recovered, and said to himself, 'What a dreadful creature is the cow! How sharp her horns! How horrible her voice!'

Bragon set out once more on his travels. He came to a sty where a big pig and six little pigs were gobbling up swede-and-acorn mash.

'Pretty pigs. Pretty pigs. Come along with me,' Bragon said to the two smallest pigs.

But the Mother Pig said, 'Snorkle-orkle-ORK!' and ran at Bragon to drive him away from her babies.

Her little eyes were so fierce and her voice so threatening that Bragon was terrified. He jumped back away from her, knocked over a bucket of pig-swill, and then ran off as far and as fast as he could go.

He sank down on a big stone and said to himself, 'Oh my, what frightful, frightening creatures are pigs! They snorkety-orkety-ork so loudly! And their eyes! Oh my goodness, what a lucky escape I have had.'

'But, oh dear, what can I take my mother?' he wondered. 'I've nothing,' and two big tears rolled down his face.

He looked over a nearby gate. Inside was a garden. In the garden were flowers. Lovely flowers – red, blue, pink and white.

Bragon opened the gate and went in. He picked one red rose, one blue love-in-a-mist, one pink carnation and one white lily.

And then he heard a voice. 'Why, Dragon-my-dear,' said the voice. 'You know, you should really ask first for the flowers.'

'I'm sorry,' said Bragon. 'But I wanted something for my mother, and I thought that she would like these flowers. May I have them, please?'

The small girl, whose name was Jane, said, 'Why of course, Dragon-my-dear.'

When he reached home, his mother asked, 'Well, Bragon? Have you had a pleasant day?'

Bragon held the flowers behind his back. 'Oh yes, mother,' he said. 'I caught . . .'

'BRAG-on,' warned his mother.

'Well, I didn't catch anything, but I was given these lovely flowers and I have brought them home for you.'

His mother smiled as she took them from him. 'Oh Bragon,' she said, 'you really are the dearest little dragon in the world.'

Slippers on

Sarah Jane and Baby John
Would not keep their slippers on;
Baby John and Sarah Jane
Always kicked them off again.

Baby John and Sarah Jane
Trod on pins and felt the pain;
Sarah Jane and Baby John
Wished they'd put their slippers on.

Stringy tale

Norah found the ball of string in the garden shed.

'Catch,' she called, throwing it to her brother, Johnny. But he missed, and it landed in a rose bush. Norah pulled it out, but one end got caught on a thorn and it began to unwind.

Johnny pulled too, but got the string round his ankle, and fell over. Norah tried to untangle him, but she only got

herself tangled up too. The more they pulled, the more tangled they got, until they were both lying on the ground, laughing and hardly able to move.

Their father and mother came out.

'They look like parcels tied up with string,' said their father. 'Shall we post them?'

'Yes,' said their mother, smiling. 'Where to? China? Land's End? The North Pole?'

'No, no!' said Norah. 'We're parcels for you.'

'I wonder what's inside?' said their father, untangling the string. 'Look! It's two children! The kind who take string from the shed and get tangled up in it. We can't have them.'

'Oh, please keep us,' said Johnny.

'All right,' said their mother, 'as long as these parcels come in now and have their tea.'

What toys are we?

Please pick me up and take a look;
Now turn my pages. I'm a _ _ _ _

Just throw me up against a wall;
I'll bounce right back, for I'm a _ _ _ _

It's bath-time. How I love to float
Across the water! I'm a _ _ _ _

Your dolls will sleep in me a lot;
I'm warm and cosy. I'm a _ _ _

Please push me and I'll travel far;
I'm very speedy. I'm a _ _ _

I'll travel there and back again;
I ride on lines, for I'm a _ _ _ _ _

The special cracker

The elves in the Christmas Cracker Factory were very excited. The King of the Elves was giving a party and they had all been invited. 'The King has ordered a very special cracker for the party tonight,' said the Chief Cracker Maker.

The elves brought out a big roll of cardboard and filled it with paper hats, tin whistles and rings.

Crinkles, the smallest cracker maker, had been working hard all day. 'I do feel tired,' he yawned. He thought he would take a rest for a few minutes, so when the others had gone to get some pretty paper he crawled inside the roll of cardboard

and fell asleep next to a paper hat!

The others came back and covered the roll with paper. 'We are all ready for the party now,' they said. 'But where is Crinkles?' They hunted everywhere but they couldn't find him. 'We'll have to go without him,' they said.

When they got to the palace the King was waiting for them. 'Before we start our tea party we will pull the big cracker,' he told them. 'Then we'll all have paper hats to put on.'

They pulled the cracker and BANG! Out tumbled Crinkles. 'You got to the party in time, after all,' they said to him.

The buttercup picnic

John was feeling grumpy because his sister had gone to a party and he was on his own.

'Let's go for a buttercup picnic,' said Mummy. 'We'll find a lovely field of buttercups and have our tea there.'

Daddy drove the car through country lanes until they had to stop because of a traffic jam.

Mummy and John got out of the car and a little boy came up to them. 'Have you seen a tortoise anywhere?' he asked. 'I'm Mark, and he's Timothy. He's woken up for the summer and I think he's wandered into the fields.'

'He has, look!' cried John pointing.

'Now we know who's holding up the traffic,' said Mummy.

Timothy tortoise ambled across the road, thoughtfully munching a buttercup. Mark ran and lifted him up.

All the drivers hooted and cheered, and then they drove on. Daddy stopped the car beside the field where the tortoise had strayed. It was full of buttercups.

The buttercup picnic was great fun, especially with Mark and Timothy as special guests.

The lost bark

Scottie the dog had lost his voice. Cat, thought it very funny. 'Why don't you look for it?' she suggested slyly.

So Scottie set off, and Cat yowled with laughter. He didn't know where to look really, just kept following his nose. It stuck in a flower. The flower buzzed and there, sitting on the end of his nose, was a bee.

'What *are* you doing?' she demanded.

Scottie's eyes crossed as he looked at her. She wore a little crown. He croaked sadly, and she stared in astonishment.

'Why,' she said, 'you've lost your voice!' He nodded, so she fell off.

'Wait there,' she said, putting her crown straight. 'I'm a queen bee, so I can help you,' and she buzzed off.

Soon, she returned, followed by a long line of her helpers, all carrying a piece of honey-comb, which they dropped at his feet.

'Lick it up,' said the queen bee, giggling at his surprise.

It was sweet, and somehow soothing.

Cat was waiting, grinning widely. 'Did you find it then?' she asked in her cattiest voice.

'Yes,' barked Scottie, 'it was in pieces!'

Cat leapt with shock – and he barked again, and gave her a good old chase.

Untidy Susie

Susie's socks are pretty and gay
But they all fell out of her drawer
one day.
Help her match each scattered pair
And find the odd one lying there.

Lucy Bodkin and the knitting

Lucy Bodkin liked rainbows but she hadn't seen one for a long time. Of course, they only come when the sun shines on rainy days and that doesn't happen very often.

'I know what I'll do,' said the funny little lady. 'I'll knit a rainbow scarf.' So she found two fat knitting needles and her big lumpy bag of rainbow coloured knitting wools.

She knitted in lots of lovely stripes – red, orange, yellow, green, light blue, dark blue and mauve. She knitted every day for a whole week until she had the *stripiest, wooliest, warmest, longest* scarf you've ever seen!

But who was to wear this fine scarf? Well, that was Lucy Bodkin's secret. She had a friend outside, a white, twinkly, jolly-looking friend with a round snowball head and a round snowball body.

'I've made you a surprise present,' she said to her twinkly friend, and she wrapped the present snuggly around his neck several times.

'Thank you very much,' said the snowman. 'I've always wanted a scarf.'

Julie's thimble

Julie had to make something for her school's Open Day. She took her sewing box into the orchard and sat down to sew a flower on a hankie.

She put on her shiny thimble so that she wouldn't prick her finger.

When Mummy called she left all her sewing things under the apple tree. 'I will come back after tea,' she said.

But when she returned to the orchard after tea she couldn't find her thimble. She looked through her sewing box and in the long grass.

'Look at that bird in the tree,' said Mummy.

'He has my thimble in his beak!' cried Julie.

'Magpies like collecting shiny things and taking them home,' explained Mummy.

It was too late to finish the sewing so Julie drew a picture instead.

Her teacher was very pleased with her picture.

She had drawn a magpie's tea party. All the birds were drinking out of little thimbles.

The donkey race

Little Grey Donkey was the smallest of six donkeys who gave rides to children on the beach. The other donkeys teased him.

'You're too small to carry the children,' they said. 'No-one wants to ride on you!'

One day the donkeys had a race across the sands. Little Grey Donkey watched the others cantering across the beach. But although little Grey Donkey was small, he had sharp eyes. He suddenly spied in the distance a *carrot*! He kicked up his heels, brayed loudly and ran faster than he had ever run before.

He ran all the way to the carrot. The other donkeys were so surprised that they stood quite still and watched him.

'Hello, have you come to share our picnic?' asked a man kindly, offering him the carrot, golden and juicy from the picnic basket.

'He's come especially to see us,' said a little girl. 'Can I ride on him? He's the loveliest donkey I've ever seen.'

Little Grey Donkey was thrilled. The girl climbed on his back and together they galloped along the sands, past all the other donkeys.

The children cheered and the little girl hugged him tightly. He had won the race – and found a friend.

Daddy's birthday present

Today was Daddy's birthday;
I only had a stone,
So I set to work with coloured pens
When I was on my own.

I drew a face and curly hair,
A mouth, two eyes and nose;
I even painted fingers
And lots of wiggly toes.

Daddy really likes it.
There's no-one else in town
Has such a jolly paper-weight
To hold his papers down.

The birds and the sleepyhead

Once upon a time there lived a plump little man and a plump little cat in a warm little house.

They had no time to do anything except eat because they could never get up early in the morning. They had breakfast at lunch-time and lunch at tea-time.

One day it was so warm indoors that they went back to sleep before giving the breakfast crumbs to the birds.

The birds were hungry. They tapped on the window.

The old man snored and the cat stretched its paws towards the fire.

All the birds sat on the window-sill and sang as loudly as they could. They made a lovely sound.

The old man opened his eyes and saw the birds singing and the cat opened his eyes and smiled.

'Will you sing loudly to us every morning so that we can get up on time?' asked the old man, giving the birds some extra crumbs.

'Yes, yes,' they sang.

So the little fat man and the little fat cat were always up in time to do all the things they wanted to do.

An elephant for an aunt?

Kate was going to spend a holiday with her Aunty Ann. Aunty wrote a letter to Kate. *I'm looking forward to your visit*, she wrote. *We'll have fun with my trunk.*

'A trunk is a long nose that belongs to an elephant,' thought Kate. 'I didn't know Aunty Ann had a trunk.'

Aunty Ann was a cousin of Kate's mother's, and Kate hadn't met her before. 'I wonder why Mum didn't tell me she had an elephant for a cousin – and that I have an elephant for an Aunt!' thought Kate.

When Aunty came to fetch Kate for her visit, Kate was surprised to see that Aunty was a lady like her mother – *not* an elephant!

Kate asked about the trunk.

'It's a travelling trunk,' explained Aunty. 'Folk don't often use trunks now, as they have suit-cases, but when I was a girl at boarding school I packed my school things into a trunk and sent it by train to the station nearest my school. I haven't looked inside the trunk for years. I thought it might be fun for us to open it together.'

Aunty's trunk was big and heavy – like a strong box with handles. Inside it, Aunty and Kate found Aunty's old school hat, her hockey-stick, some gym-shoes, a blazer and some books.

'May I play with them, please, and pretend I'm a school-girl?' asked Kate.

Kate and Aunty played the school game every day. Aunty was fun, and Kate was glad she didn't have an elephant for an aunt, after all.

Bumbly Bee

There was once a bee who was very, very clumsy. He tripped over rose-thorns. He tumbled into dew drops. In fact, he bumbled and stumbled about so much that his friends laughed at him and called him Bumbly Bee.

One rainy day in the rose garden, he bumped into a fat old spider.

'Clumsy insect,' hissed the spider, 'why don't you look where you're flying!'

Just then, Bumbly Bee heard a voice calling out: 'Please, *please*, help me. The spider has trapped me.'

He looked – and there on a leaf was a little butterfly caught in the spider's nasty web. Bumbly Bee flew across at once to rescue her.

But he was so clumsy, he bumped straight into a big red rose. The wet rose petals shook themselves, and all the rain-drops fell down in a shower over the spider. The fat old spider gave such a great sneeze that he blew himself right off the leaf!

Quickly, Bumbly Bee unwound the web from the butterfly's wings, and helped her to a safe place. The grateful butterfly told everyone how he had rescued her from the spider's web.

And Bumbly Bee's friends never laughed at his clumsiness again.

The kite flyers

Swish, swish, swish went the bright yellow kite as it raced across the sky, twisting and somersaulting over its long, flapping tail.

John was on the end of the strings, pulling them to send the kite wherever he pleased. WOOOSH – it plunged suddenly to the ground, then righted itself, hovered and raced up to the clouds again.

'Wheee,' called a voice nearby. 'That was fun. You're a good kite flyer.'

A man was walking up the hill towards him. He had a big smile on his face and he was carrying a canvas bag. Kneeling down on the grass, he opened the bag and took out six kites, all different shapes and sizes and beautiful colours. The one John liked best was a giant butterfly.

'I made all these myself,' the man told John, 'and I'm trying them out for the first time. Would you like to help me?'

They stayed up there on the hill, flying kites all afternoon. As John ran off home for tea, the man called out, 'Come back next Saturday, John. I will have finished another kite by then.'

'I will,' John called back happily. 'I might even try making one myself, and we can have a competition.'

The brave knight

Long ago a brave knight called Sir Gareth rode towards a king's palace. He wondered why everyone looked sad. 'My daughter, Princess Mirabelle, has vanished,' said the King.

'I will search for her,' promised Sir Gareth. He rode over hill and dale, asking many people, but no-one had seen the princess. At last he reached a cottage where an old woman lived.

'If you will chop my wood, draw my water and plough my field, I will help you in your search,' she said. So Sir Gareth did as she bade him, until darkness fell.

'By the light of this candle you can see into the four corners of the kingdom,' she told him. Sir Gareth saw by its light a great castle. Inside was Princess Mirabelle. 'That is the Black Knight's enchanted castle,' said the old woman.

Sir Gareth rode on until he reached the castle, but a magic thorn hedge grew all round it. Each time he cut it with his sword it grew thicker. In despair he lit the candle to look again at the princess. The flame touched the hedge and quickly burnt through it.

The Black Knight came galloping out and Sir Gareth fought him until he was beaten forever. So the king gave Sir Gareth half his kingdom and Princess Mirabelle's hand in marriage, and they lived happily ever after.

The old rose

The rose tree was very old, and nowadays she had only a few buds and flowers. Now, there were bright new bushes, and some even had different coloured roses on the same bush.

Then, the family left the house. The grass and the weeds grew fast. The old rose felt sad.

But a new family moved in – mother, father, and a little boy and girl.

'I am so pleased,' sighed the rose. 'I love children.'

'The roses are lovely,' said the mother.

'Except that old one,' frowned the father. 'I'll root it out.'

The rose was heart-broken! The family didn't want her.

Suddenly, she heard another voice. 'This rose tree is the only one whose flowers have a scent.' An old lady cupped a rose in her hand and buried her face in its scented petals. It was the children's great-grandmother.

'A rose is nothing if it has no scent. Please keep this tree.'

'Of course,' smiled the father.

And the old lady cared for the rose, watered it, and fed its roots, and now it has more blooms than ever.

Loch monsters

*Some folk like to hunt wild boar
Others prefer the fox,
But I like hunting monsters
That dwell in Scottish lochs.*

*Their necks are long and slender,
Their heads like ostrich eggs;
Their teeth are sharp and pointed,
But they haven't any legs.*

*That's why they stay in water
And never come to land,
For if they did, they'd find it quite
Impossible to stand.*

*Descriptions of these monsters
Are very hard to get.
That's why I can't give details,
For I haven't caught one yet.*

Ronald Robot has a rest

Ronald was a mechanical man who had been invented by Professor Pete. He was a robot, and could be made to do things. Professor Pete had invented Ronald because he wanted someone to do his work.

Ronald was a good worker. Each day, he would get the breakfast ready, wash up, make the beds, do the washing and ironing, the shopping, cleaning and gardening.

Ronald had worked so hard for such a long time, that Professor Pete decided Ronald should take a rest. He drove Ronald to the seaside, and left him at a hotel where he was to spend two weeks' holiday. After a few days, Professor Pete returned to see how Ronald was enjoying himself.

'I expect he likes sunbathing, the sand, paddling, and relaxing in a deck-chair,' thought Professor Pete.

To his surprise, he found Ronald looking miserable.

'I don't like sunbathing,' Ronald said. 'The sun makes my metal too hot. The sand gets into my works. Paddling makes my metal rust. If I sit about in a deckchair, my works seize up. It was kind of you to offer me a rest, but I was specially made to work. Will you take me home, so I can get on with my usual jobs?'

'Of course! Get into the car,' said Professor Pete. 'I'm glad you're coming home again to look after things, but what an unusual fellow you are! Fancy preferring hard work to holidays.'

Fairy Thistledown's lost handbag

One day the Pixie Pedlar called at Fairy Thistledown's cottage. He carried a trayful of beads and ribbons and lots of baskets, pots and pans. 'Would you like to buy a kettle or a saucepan?' he asked.

Fairy Thistledown looked at his tray. 'I would like some of that blue ribbon for my hair,' she said. 'It will match the dress I bought when I went to the shops this morning. Wait while I get some money.'

Fairy Thistledown looked all round the house for her handbag. But she couldn't find it anywhere. 'I must have dropped it on my way back from the shops,' she cried.

They both searched along the road, looking everywhere. Then the Pixie Pedlar saw something hanging from a bush. It was Fairy Thistledown's handbag. Inside was a baby fieldmouse.

Then Mrs Fieldmouse came along with her apron full of berries. 'I found the handbag lying in the road,' she said. 'So I popped the baby in there so that he wouldn't get lost while I collected food for my larder.'

The Pixie Pedlar found a basket for all Mrs Fieldmouse's berries and a tiny cradle for the baby fieldmouse. So Fairy Thistledown got her handbag back and she was able to buy some hair ribbon to match her new dress.

Jolly moves house

Peter took carrots to his carthorse friend, Jolly.

Jolly's owner was there, putting leather harness on him.

'What *are* you doing?' asked Peter. 'I thought Jolly didn't work now.'

Mr Barnaby laughed. 'That's right! But the noisy engines today, often don't match up to my Jolly!' He patted the horse fondly. 'Old Mrs Cotton is moving from her cottage, and the removal van has broken down.'

'Surely,' said Peter, 'Jolly can't pull a removal van?'

'Goodness no!' laughed Mr Barnaby, But come and see what he *can* do.'

Peter beamed as together, they led Jolly down to the farmyard, and backed him into a large cart.

Jolly stepped eagerly, knowing he was needed again.

At Mrs Cotton's cottage, the removal van had its bonnet up.

'Oh – I'm so glad to see you!' cried the old lady, thankfully.

They lifted all her furniture out of the van, and into the cart.

Then, Jolly moved his huge limbs, and pulled the big pile across the village. Peter held his reins.

'I just don't know how to thank you,' said Mrs Cotton, when all her furniture was safely inside her new home.

'Don't thank us,' they said together. 'Thank Jolly!'

Who's a pretty boy?

Joey the green budgie lived in a cage by the dining-room window. He played with his toys all day. He had a swing, a ladder and a bell.

But one day, he just sat on his perch staring out of the window. He was lonely.

Roy came into the room: 'Hello, Joey! Who's a pretty boy?'

Joey said nothing.

Roy looked sadly at him. It was Saturday. He stared at his pocket money. What should he buy? He looked at poor Joey again and then he hurried to the pet shop, and came home clutching a paper bag.

He hung the little mirror beside the perch. Joey stared into it. A handsome green bird stared back at him.

'Who's a pretty boy?' said Joey, talking to his own reflection.

'Who's a pretty boy?' said the budgie in the mirror. Joey wasn't lonely anymore. He had a new friend.

The fire that wouldn't go out

Mrs Jones's doorbell rang.

Now, Mrs Jones was a cold, proud woman. She opened the door and saw a poor old lady standing there.

'What do you want?' asked Mrs Jones.

'May I sit at your fireside for five minutes and get warm?' asked the stranger.

'Certainly not,' snapped Mrs Jones. 'I don't want a dirty old lady in my nice clean kitchen.'

'May your fire never go out,' said the old lady, and then she disappeared.

Mrs Jones shut the door with a bang. In the kitchen the fire was burning brightly, and Mrs Jones didn't need to put on any more coal that day. Next day, the fire still burned. And the next. *And* the next. And still no coal was needed.

Well, a magic fire is fine in winter but when the warm days of spring and summer come . . .

'Please try and put that wretched fire out!' said Mrs Jones to her husband.

But water wouldn't put out the fire.

An orange orange

If I had an orange orange,
And I cut it into two,
Would that be in halves then—
A piece for me and you?

And if those orange pieces,
Were cut across once more,
Would that be in quarters—
An orange piece for four?

Well, I like an orange orange,
So I think I'll leave it be;
I'll pretend I have a single one—
A whole one, just for me!

The days grew hotter and so did the fire, and so did Mr and Mrs Jones. At last they could bear it no longer.

'We must move house,' said Mrs Jones. Mr Jones nodded.

So they moved house and on the day they left the magic fire went out.

Wash day

Sarah loved helping her mother with the washing. She helped sort out the coloured clothes from the whites and she measured out the soap powder carefully.

One day Mother said, 'The washing machine has gone wrong. We'll have to take the washing to the launderette.' So they filled the shopping basket on wheels with the dirty washing and they walked to the shops.

It was fun putting the silver coins in the large automatic machine and seeing the washing twirling round faster and faster, and the soap suds covering the little glass door. When the machine stopped it was time to take the clothes out and put them in the drier.

'I'll help you, Mummy,' said Sarah. It was nice and warm in the launderette and they had time for mother to read her a story while the clothes dried.

Soon all the clothes were dry and Sarah helped fold them neatly.

'I do like it when our washing machine won't work,' Sarah said. 'It's fun going to the launderette.'

The pinka-ponka, binka-bonka machine

The professor stood back and looked at his latest invention in the garage.

'It's beautiful,' he sighed. 'I just can't wait to try it out.'

Just then his wife called from the house, 'are you busy, dear?'

'O-oh, she wants me to do the dishes,' the professor moaned. 'Here's my chance to use my invention.' Then he answered, 'Very busy. Can't you hear?' And he turned on his machine.

Flashing lights came on, lighting up the garage. Wheels began to spin. Gears began to grind and the latest invention went 'pinka-ponka, binka-bonka.'

Louder and louder it pinked and ponked and binked and bonked.

'It's all right then,' his wife shouted. 'I know you're busy, dear. All those funny noises convince me.'

The professor laughed, 'It works. It does what it's supposed to do – it makes busy noises. And it saves me from house-hold chores.'

Inside the house his wife went back to her television set. 'So he misses his favourite programme,' she said to her-self. 'I'm sure he thought I wanted him to do the dishes. He didn't fool me a bit with all that funny noise.'

Tall, small and spikey

An elf is as tall as a toadstool,
A pixie's as small as a daisy,
A hedgehog is spikey and spiney
And a tortoise is terribly lazy.

Sally and the starlings

Sally lived in a big block of flats. And when she looked out, she could see the town hall clock.

The town hall clock was very big, and on bright, clear days Sally could see the hands on it. In the mornings it would wake Sally up by striking eight times: dong, dong, dong, dong, dong, dong, dong, dong . . .

But one morning the clock didn't strike. It had stopped.

Then Sally saw lots of birds sitting on the hands of the clock. So she put on her clothes and went to the town hall.

'Those starlings have stopped it,' said a man in a big yellow lorry with a long ladder. Then he went up the ladder and started the clock again.

Sally was glad to hear the clock strike eight times the next morning. And when she went to the window and looked out, she saw lots of starlings chirping and chattering on the grass round the flats.

'I'll give them some breadcrumbs,' she laughed. 'That will keep them away from the town hall clock.'

Sir Bumbelot and Sir Dunceymor

Once there were two old knights. One was short and fat. He was called Sir Bumbelot. The other was tall and skinny. His name was Sir Dunceymor.

And all day long they hunted dragons. Dragons were their hobby, their love, their life.

In great thick armour and with long sharp weapons they roamed the country-side looking and looking. But they never found a dragon. Then one day they put on their best armour and chose their finest weapons. 'Today we will find a dragon!' they shouted.

Up hill and down hill they trudged until, suddenly, it began to rain.

'Our armour will rust!' cried Sir Bumbelot.

'I see a cave!' shouted Sir Dunceymor.

Off in the distance was a big opening. Great pointed rocks lined its entrance. Smoke trickled slowly out of its mouth. The knights ran inside.

'Isn't it warm,' laughed Sir Bumbelot.

'Couldn't have chosen a nicer place,' Sir Dunceymor smiled.

The rain stopped. The two knights stepped out.

'I've a feeling we're close to a dragon today,' they shouted as they tramped off.

The cave shut its mouth. Then it opened its eyes. 'Pooh! I've nothing to fear from those two,' the dragon laughed to himself.

The mischievous wind

The wind came rushing
Through the town,
Like horses at the races . . .
What did he do?
Find what blew
Into strange and funny places.

Gunfight at sunset

'So Black Bart is coming to take your ranch, eh?' the Two-gun Kid drawled.

'Yes,' the Fair Helen answered, 'and then he'll steal my horses and cattle.'

'We'll see about that!' Like greased lightning Two-gun drew his pistols from their holsters and spun them around.

'He's big,' Fair Helen cried timidly.

'The bigger they come, the harder they fall,' laughed Two-gun, cocking his cowboy hat forward with a pistol barrel.

'He's tough,' Fair Helen said shakily.

'Not too tough for flying lead,' Two-gun smiled confidently.

'I hear him now,' Fair Helen cried.

A door banged shut in the distance. Great feet went *clump, clump.*

Two-gun thrust his pistols into their holsters. He spread his legs wide apart and stood there, two hands just over the pistol butts.

A great shadow fell on Two-gun and Fair Helen.

Two-gun drew both pistols. 'Bang! Bang!' he cried. 'Got you, Black Bart!'

'Black Bart, am I?' father laughed. 'Well, Black Bart says it's sunset and time for all cowboys and cowgirls to be in bed.'

And off to bed they went.

Daffy's slide

Daffy the elf had made a long slide on the path that led down the hill to Daisy Dell. 'Whee!' he shouted as he slid down. 'This is great fun.'

Just then, two of the gnomes who lived in Daisy Dell came over the hill. One was carrying a basket of eggs and the other had a big bottle of milk. But, oh dear! No sooner had they stepped on Daffy's slide than they fell over. The

eggs were smashed and the milk was spilt. It made an awful mess.

The gnomes were very cross. They were so angry that they chased Daffy right through the wood.

The gnomes were shouting so loudly that they woke up Daffy's friend, Ossie Owl. 'What's Daffy been up to now?' he hooted. 'I must rescue him before the gnomes catch him.'

Ossie found a tree branch with lots of icicles on it. It hung right across the woodland path. As soon as Daffy had run underneath it, Ossie pecked off the icicles and they fell into the ground. They blocked the path so that the gnomes could not get by.

Daffy raced safely home to his hollow tree. 'You really are a silly elf,' scolded Ossie. 'Perhaps that will teach you not to make a slide in such a dangerous place again.'

A lion in the garden

Squirrel stopped and listened.

'I can hear a lion roaring,' she said to herself. 'I must go and tell Rabbit.'

She ran to the grassy bank. 'There's a lion in the garden,' she cried.

Rabbit, with his big ears, listened. 'We must go and tell Mouse,' he said.

They ran to the hedge. 'Come quickly,' they said. 'There's a lion in the garden.'

Mouse peeped out of her hole and twitched her whiskers. 'We'd better tell Owl,' she squeaked. 'He'll know what to do.' So they all ran to tell Owl. Owl was having a nap, and wasn't at all pleased at being disturbed. 'Don't be silly,' he said crossly. 'Lions don't live in gardens.' But he flew down and they all crept quietly through the long grass.

Suddenly, they stopped!

Sitting in the middle of the lawn, fast asleep, was old Tom the Gardener.

He was snoring his head off.

'There's your lion,' said Owl.

How they all laughed!

Harry the hospital horse

Nicola was given a wooden horse with wheels for her third birthday. She called him Harry. She could sit on Harry, and ride him round the garden, or push him along by his handle. Nicola loved Harry, but by the time she was six years old, Harry was too small for her.

Harry was surprised, when he heard Nicola's mummy say, 'I think we'll send Harry to hospital.'

Harry was put into a car and driven through the town to the hospital. 'I know I'm not used any longer, but I'm not ill,' thought Harry. 'Why are they sending me to hospital?'

Harry was lifted from the car and taken into the childrens' ward. There Harry realised that he had been brought to the hospital so that the children who were getting better, and were well enough to play, could play with *him*. The small children loved riding him and pushing him, just as Nicola had once done.

'I think you are going to be busy and happy and useful here, Harry,' whispered Nicola.

'I think so, too,' smiled Harry.

Alexander's bedtime band

Alexander was a boy who loved music. He had a drum with drumsticks, a trumpet to blow and a shaker to shake. He also had something called a xylophone with two little hammers to make tinkle-tonk sort of music. 'Xylophone' was an interesting word to say and Mummy said it began with the letter X which made it even more interesting because Alexander knew that his name had an X in it too.

Alexander thought it would be wonderful to hear all his musical things played together in a band. The trouble was he didn't have enough hands to use them all at the same time!

But one bedtime he had a great idea. If Teddybear and the rest of his friends sat in a row on the bedroom floor they could each play something different. They could be a band! So Alexander gave the drum to Teddybear, the trumpet to Elephant, the shaker to Gonk and the xylophone to Rabbit.

After that he climbed into bed and just before he fell asleep something quite magical happened. He was absolutely sure he could hear the sound of music . . .

POM-TIDDLY-POM-POM!
TOOT TOOT!
TINKLE-TONK-TINKLE-
* TONK!*
BOOM BANG BOOM!

Happy birthday

Farmer Brown was feeding the chickens early in the morning. 'I'm ready for breakfast,' he said to Nell, his dog.

Bertha the cow looked over the fence: 'MOOO.' Miss Pig looked up. 'Do you know what day it is?' asked Bertha.

'Monday,' replied Miss Pig.

'It's Farmer Brown's birthday,' said Bertha. 'We should give him a surprise, what can we do?'

'I'll call the other animals. They might have some ideas,' said Miss Pig.

'How about a bunch of daisies,' suggested Ben the horse.

'How about a brown egg,' clucked Harriet the hen.

'They are very nice ideas,' said Bertha, 'but it must be *very* special.'

'I could sing *Happy Birthday*,' said Rupert Robin.

'That's it!' shouted Sammy the Donkey. 'We will all sing.'

'I think that's wonderful,' said Bertha. 'Rupert can teach us.'

Rupert Robin flew onto Bertha's head and sang *Happy Birthday*.

Farmer Brown came into the farmyard. All his animals gathered around him.

'Eee-awe,' sang Sammy.
'Oink,' sang Miss Pig.
'Cluck,' sang Harriet Hen.
'Neigh,' sang Ben the horse.
And 'Moooo,' sang Bertha.
Farmer Brown was delighted.

My week

On Monday I played with my blue,
    bouncing ball,
It bounced so high it went over the wall.

On Tuesday I painted, because it was
    wet,
A picture of Pussy, my very own pet.

On Wednesday I went to see Peter,
    next-door,
And we had his toys out all over the
    floor.

On Thursday I fell off my bike, it hurt
    me,
So I had a plaster put over my knee.

On Friday I rode on a bus to the shops
And bought a big bagful of chocolate
    drops.

On Saturday, in the playground,
    I tried
To see how fast I could whizz down
    the slide.
But Sunday I know was the very best
    day,
I went to my Granny's, oh, such a
    long way,
She knew I was coming and made just
    for me
Her own special cakes that I like for
    my tea.

The school bus

School was over for the day and mothers waited at the gate for their children. But there were ten children who lived too far from school for parents to collect them, and so a bus called for them. Today the bus was late – very late. But the ten children waited for it and when it at last arrived, they climbed inside.

'Where to?' asked the driver.

Now this was an odd question, for the driver knew exactly where they all lived.

'Home, of course,' they answered.

'Hoho,' laughed the driver. And then the children saw his face. It was not their usual driver but a pixie with a very friendly grin.

'Home it shall be,' he laughed, and the engine started up with a tremendous roar. Then, *up and away* went the school bus – into the sky and over the roof-tops, faster than any aeroplane. The driver turned to the children. 'Like it?' he asked. '*Oh yes!*' they shouted. 'It's wonderful.'

The school bus began bouncing up and down on the clouds. It rose high. It dipped low. Suddenly there appeared a beautiful rainbow. The school bus flew *up* the rainbow, *over* the rainbow, and *down* the rainbow. At last it came to rest on Earth.

Then the children saw that the pixie was no longer in the driver's seat. Joe, their usual driver, was there. And the school bus took them safely home.

The Parallelephant

Of all the creatures I have known
There's one that stands out on its own,
A beast that really takes the prize
For its unusual shape and size,
An animal not found in zoos,
That sometimes trumpets, sometimes
coos.
It's clumsy, far from elegant –
It's called the Parallelephant.

To capture one try mumbo-jumbo,
But do not ever call him Dumbo.
I'm warning you, he'll understand
Because he's been to Disney-land.
His curious trunk you're bound to spot,
For he can tie it in a knot;
And parallel from head to feet,
He has a job to make ends meet.

A kitten for a pet

'Please, can we have a kitten of our own?'
Cathy and Liza asked their mummy one
day when they got home from school.

Mummy said she thought it was a very
nice idea, now they were old enough to
look after a pet properly. 'I know,' she
said, 'when I collect you both from
school tomorrow, we'll go and see if the
pet shop has any kittens for sale.'

Mummy then suggested they should
get everything ready, so Liza found a
small carton and Cathy screwed up some
newspaper to place in the bottom and
covered it with one of her doll's blankets
so that the kitten would have a nice, soft
bed to sleep in. Then the girls sorted
through some old crockery and selected
two dainty saucers for the kitten to eat
from.

Just as they finished, they heard
Daddy's cheerful voice call from the hall.
'Hello, everyone, I've got a lovely
surprise for you!'

They all rushed into the hall just as
Daddy was putting a box down on the
floor. He opened the lid and Cathy and
Liza could hardly believe their eyes. Out
stepped the fluffiest, tiniest, most beautiful black and white kitten they had ever
seen.

'I thought it would be a nice idea for
you two girls to have a pet of your very
own,' Daddy said.

Cathy and Liza started to laugh, and
so did Mummy and Daddy. It seemed as
though the kitten had been meant for
them.

Emily's friend

Today was Sunday and Emily was going to visit her friend Alexander. Alexander lived in the cottage opposite the church. He had lots of animals including a goat, and Emily loved to go with him when he took the goat for a walk.

The wind was very cold so Emily put on her woollen hat, scarf and mittens and made her way up the hill towards the church. When she reached the cottage Alexander's grandmother gave them both a large mug of hot chocolate and some home-baked biscuits. When they had finished and were both feeling really warm inside, they put on their woolly hats and went out to collect Alice the goat. Alice was very beautiful, Emily thought. She had a lovely long coat, gentle eyes, and a big rubbery nose that she loved you to scratch. They all set off down the lane towards the heath. Soon Alexander tied a long rope onto the goat's collar and held the other end tight in his hand. Alice trotted along, free to go where she liked, and Emily and Alexander skipped and ran beside her. When she stopped to eat they stood and watched while she chewed up thorns and thistles. The children laughed and were glad they preferred icecream and jellies.

Wheels!

Now I'm three I have a tricycle
And ride around the garden.
When I'm eight I'll have a bicycle
And pedal down the pavement.
And when I'm grown-up like Pa
I'll have a super motor car.
Then I'll be able to drive SO FAR!

When they got back to the cottage after their big walk they put Alice back in her shed and patting her goodbye they crossed the garden to the kitchen door. 'Tea's all ready,' said Grandma as she let them in. There was a lovely fire burning in the big open grate and there were hot buttered scones and a big pot of tea on the table. It was very cosy.

When they had finished tea Emily said goodbye to Alexander and his grandmother and ran nearly all the way home. Pasha, her dog, and the cats were waiting for her at the garden gate. They were all very pleased that Emily was back and went into the kitchen to have some supper.

As Emily sat back and watched all her little animals busily eating she smiled and thought what a lovely day it had been.

The poor tailor

There once was a poor tailor who packed all his belongings into a bundle and set off to seek his fortune.

The first day he saw an old woman sitting by the roadside, sighing because she had torn her cloak. 'I'll mend your cloak,' said the tailor and his needle wove in and out until the cloak looked like new.

The old woman took a spindle from her basket and began to spin cobwebs from the hedges into thread, so the tailor guessed she was a witch. But he thanked her for the spindle of thread and went on his way.

The second day he heard someone crying bitterly. He looked among the grass and saw a fairy who had torn her wing. 'I'll mend your wing,' he said, and his needle wove in and out until the wing was like new.

'I will weave your thread into cloth,' said the fairy. So using a tiny loom, she wove the thread into silvery cloth. The tailor thanked her and went on his way.

The third day he came to a city where everyone was merry-making. 'The King and Queen are to be crowned,' he was told.

The tailor went straight to the palace and asked for the cloth to be shown to the Queen. 'My coronation robes shall be made of this beautiful cloth,' she commanded.

So the poor tailor became the Royal Tailor and soon made his fortune.

Dilly Dally and Dabble

'You can't really mean it,' said Dilly Dally and Dabble Drake, looking up at Farmer Bill with sad eyes. 'You can't be sending us away tomorrow.'

'It's true,' replied Farmer Bill unhappily. 'Farmer John is coming to collect you at ten o'clock in the morning because he wants to have you on his farm.'

Dilly Dally and Dabble couldn't believe it, and neither could their farm friends who gathered round when they heard the news. Wise old Porker Pig was the last to hear, and as he trotted up to the crowd of animals, he called, 'Don't worry, I know what to do.' And they all clapped and cheered when they heard his plan.

Next morning, at ten o'clock when Farmer Bill and Farmer John arrived at the duckpond, they couldn't believe their eyes. There, in a circle around the pond, stood all the farm animals, glaring at them. And, safe in the middle of the pond, sat Dilly Dally and Dabble.

'Well, I'll be!' exclaimed Farmer Bill.

'I think you'd better keep your ducks, Bill,' laughed Farmer John. 'They're too popular.'

That evening, when Farmer Bill was feeding the ducks, he gave them a pat and said, 'You're a crafty pair, and I'm certainly glad of it.'

All change

Tim had a fort, with a drawbridge that went up and down, and some fine soldiers. His sister, Tina had a dolls' house with a little family she called the Twiggles.

One night, while the children slept, a mischievous elf put a spell on the dolls' house and the fort so that all the little toy people came to life.

'We are tired of keeping guard in our fort,' cried the soldiers. They let down the drawbridge and marched into the room.

'We are tired of living in the dolls' house,' sighed the Twiggles. So the Twiggle family stepped out through their green front door on to the carpet.

The Twiggles and the soldiers met and said, 'How do you do?' Then the soldiers visited the dolls' house. 'It is very small and cramped,' they thought.

The Twiggle family crossed the drawbridge into the fort. 'What a big, draughty place!' they shivered.

As the sun rose, the spell was broken and the little people could no longer move or speak.

When Tim and Tina woke, they were astonished to find the soldiers in the dolls' house and the Twiggles in the fort.

'How did they get there?' gasped Tim. 'I don't know,' whispered Tina.

But we know, don't we?

Sally makes an animal

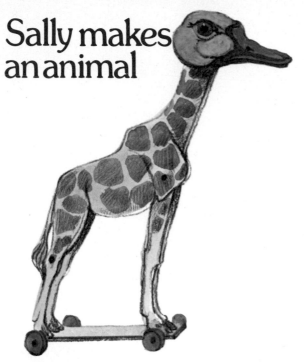

One day, when Sally went to see Mr Luke, the toy maker, she found his workshop empty. Mr Luke made wooden animals on wheels, that you pulled along with a string, and there were bits of them lying on the bench, waiting to be stuck together.

Sally decided to help Mr Luke. She picked up a duck's head and put some glue on it, and stuck it to one of the bodies. It looked like a very strange duck, because the body had four long legs.

When Mr Luke came back, he stared at the duck in surprise. Then he burst out laughing, and said, 'You've stuck a duck's head on a giraffe's body.'

'Oh, I am sorry,' said Sally.

'Never mind,' said Mr Luke. 'You've invented a new animal. What shall we call it? I know – the Ducky-Raffe.'

'The Ducky-Raffe,' said Sally, delighted.

'You can have him if you like,' said Mr Luke.

'Oh, thank you,' exclaimed Sally.

And she walked home, leading the Ducky-Raffe on its string.

Aunt Sarah and Aunt Sally

David was staying with his Aunt Sarah who lived at the seaside. It was fun to dig in the sand, paddle in the sea and watch the boats, while Aunt Sarah sat in a deckchair in the sun or chatted to her friend the boatman.

One afternoon Aunt Sarah said, 'Pick up your bucket and spade, David, we're going to see Aunt Sally.'

'Who's Aunt Sally?' asked David doubtfully. 'Is she old?'

'Come along the beach and see,' said Aunt Sarah with a twinkle in her eye.

'Does she live on the beach then?' asked David, more interested now. 'In a sandcastle?'

Aunt Sarah just laughed. They walked along the hot sands but David couldn't see anyone that looked like an Aunt Sally.

'There!' cried Aunt Sarah, pointing at a gay rowing boat at the water's edge.

Aunt Sarah's friend the boatman was sitting inside and, written along the boat, were the words:

AUNT SALLY

'A boat!' cried David.

'Not a bit old,' said Aunt Sarah. 'Quite new, in fact, and waiting to give you a ride.'

The birthday tea

It was Edward Bear's birthday and Wendy had prepared a special birthday tea. Wendy was a beautiful doll. In fact, Edward Bear thought she was the most beautiful doll in the whole world.

Wendy had sent Edward out on an errand and the toys were all busy laying the doll's table so that it would be a surprise when he returned.

Jolly brought in the bright red tablecloth and napkins and the Rabbits bustled through clattering knives, forks and spoons. Only Elephant was strong enough to carry the big pile of plates. Lion followed with a steaming hot apple pie and then Pussycat set down a jug of tasty cream. Last of all came Wendy, carrying the birthday cake. She set it down in the middle of the table and lit the candles. What a lovely sight it was!

At last the door opened and Edward Bear walked in. 'HAPPY BIRTHDAY,' they all shouted. Edward couldn't believe his eyes. He was so happy!

Wendy came over and gave him a big birthday kiss. That made it the very best birthday he had ever had.

My bag of sweets

I had twenty sweets in all :
Four for Peter, four for Paul ;
Jane is greedy, she took eight.
I saw Betty at the gate—
She looked sad. I gave her three,
How many does that leave for me?

Quacker's adventure

Quacker was a yellow rubber duck, and he loved bedtime because Billy, the little boy who owned him, floated him in the bath.

One day, Billy's family went to the sea-side. Billy took Quacker and floated him on the shallow waves.

'Oh, this is fun!' thought Quacker. 'Much more fun than the bath.'

Then, Billy's daddy said he'd teach Billy how to swim. He held him around the waist while Billy pushed against the waves with his arms and legs.

Quacker was bouncing on the waves too. At first, he enjoyed it, but then he saw that the tide was going out, and each wave that rolled over washed him farther from the beach.

'Time for tea,' said Billy's Daddy.

Billy looked round for Quacker. 'Daddy, Quacker is drifting out to sea — save him!'

Billy's daddy swam to Quacker's rescue.

'I don't like the sea, after all,' Quacker thought. 'I'd much rather swim in the bath.'

The Happy Birthday Cake Baker

Jenny Jolly's best birthday surprise was a cake — a great big cake with yellow icing and a bright red ribbon. All it said on the card was:

'To Jenny Jolly, from The Happy Birthday Cake Baker.'

Jenny was very puzzled. Who was The Happy Birthday Cake Baker? She knew it wasn't Mummy or Daddy or Mrs Robbins next-door, and it couldn't be Auntie Sal because she was on holiday. So who could it be?

By five o'clock, all the guests had arrived for her fancy dress party, and Jenny was to cut the cake. Mummy lit the candles and turned out the lights, and Jenny blew her hardest. When the lights came on again, who should be standing at Jenny's side but her Granny — in a baker's white hat and apron! On the apron, in big letters, was written:

THE HAPPY
BIRTHDAY CAKE BAKER

'I thought I'd come in fancy dress, too,' laughed Granny.

And when they had tried the cake, all the children agreed that Granny was the best Happy Birthday Cake Baker they knew.

The little mouse

The little mouse dashed across the floor and made a dive for the hole in the wall.

'Phew,' he sighed, panting for breath, 'that was a near thing. A kitten in the house. Something has to be done. I must think of a plan.'

'I've got it,' he cried, leaping up suddenly. 'I'll make a toy mouse,' and collecting an old blanket, some buttons, thread and a long piece of string, he set to work. 'This'll fool him,' he chuckled. When he had finished he sat the toy mouse just inside the hole so the kitten could see it. Then he went through his little house to the back door and squeezed through the hole out into the kitchen.

He could see the kitten sitting in the other room, it's eyes still glued on the toy mouse.

The little mouse took some food from the larder and crept quietly back home again. He collected his toy mouse and put him on the bed.

'You're going to be very useful, my friend,' he said and, sitting back in the chair, put his feet on the table, chuckled to himself and bit into a large piece of cheese.

Who are we?

Please do not sit on us, children,
Or you'll quickly jump off us again.
Resist any longing to stroke us,
Can't you youngsters imagine the pain?
Underfoot you may very well find us.
Please treat us with caution because
If you kick us you'll surely regret it;
No one knows how much damage we cause.
Examine this verse with great care;
Some readers will notice us there!

Lee's motor-bike

A man with a motor-bike
Came to the door,
Such a shining machine
And Lee touched it, with awe.

'Come off!' yelled the man,
'It isn't for boys!'
And Lee longed for a bike
That made such a big noise.

With a set of old handle-bars,
He mounted a wall –
'Brum-brum! brum-brum!'
Came his motor-bike call.

Now he roars where he fancies,
Ignores all his toys:
For he's riding a bike
That makes such a big noise.

Wet afternoon

It was a very wet afternoon. Polly was just beginning to feel bored and was wondering what game to play next, when her mummy had a lovely idea.

'Let's make some cakes, Polly. We could make a whole tray of little cakes.'

'Oh, yes please, Mummy.' Polly was quite delighted. Nothing could be more fun than to feel cosy in the warm kitchen and, when the cakes were in the oven, to sniff the delicious smells of the cakes as they cooked.

Best of all, Polly's mummy always let her decorate the cakes and, of course, Polly always ate one while they were still warm, just to make sure they were as good as they looked!

This afternoon Polly wanted to make the cakes especially pretty. Mummy made her some icing which Polly had been taught to spread over the cakes with a wet knife. Then came the real fun — popping on the glacé cherries, sprinkling on the hundreds and thousands and making patterns with small sweets.

Just as Polly was putting the last cherry on the last cake, the doorbell rang. Mummy was soon back and, who should walk in with her, but Granny and Aunty Jo.

'Looks as though we called at just the right time!' Granny laughed.

The surprise

Sally was very excited. Soon, her mummy was going to have a baby, and Sally could hardly wait for her new brother or sister to arrive. For weeks Sally had been helping her mummy and daddy to get ready. They had painted the nursery a bright yellow and filled the tiny bedroom with everything the baby would need.

The day arrived when Sally's mummy had to go to hospital. Her granny came round to look after Sally.

Sally had a lovely day. Her granny played with her all morning, then she cooked Sally's favourite lunch. They went to the park in the afternoon and by the time they arrived home they were getting excited, in case there was any news.

Just as they arrived Sally's daddy pulled up in the car. He threw open the door and there was a big smile on his face.

'You'll never guess what has happened — Mummy has had twins! Now you have a baby brother and a baby sister, too.'

Sally and Granny laughed with joy. Sally had never dreamt she could be so lucky. But that night she did dream — about all the fun she would have with the twins when they came home.

Lisa's lovely picture

Lisa painted a picture one day. She painted a golden sun, a dark blue lake, green trees, pink and white flowers on yellow grass, and a pale blue sky.

It was such a lovely picture that Lisa decided to send it to Fairyland. She wrote *To the Fairies* on her picture, and took it outside and let it blow away in the wind.

Lisa's sister, Frances, didn't like the idea.

'If your picture does reach Fairyland, it will be too big for the fairies,' said Frances. 'They couldn't get it inside one of their tiny houses.'

Lisa went to bed disappointed, but that night, a fairy visited her. The fairy waved her wand over Lisa to make Lisa fly and away they went to Fairyland.

'Look what has happened to your picture,' the fairy said. 'It blew up against the high wall of the Fairyland picnic place. It covers the whole wall, and it's pasted there so that when fairies come here they feel as if they are in a beautiful park. Now even on dull days, our picnic place looks cheerful and we have a bright, golden sun!'

When Lisa woke up in bed, the next morning, she wondered if her trip to Fairyland had been a dream, but she never did see her picture again, so she felt sure it really had arrived in Fairyland to brighten the fairies' picnic place.

Inch Elf has a visitor

Inch Elf's friend Oliver Otter was always busy working, so Inch was often lonely.

There were lots of toadstool houses in Buttercup Wood, but the elves that lived there were all much taller than Inch, and they were rather rude to him.

'You are much too small to play with us,' the elves told Inch.

Oliver Otter told Inch not to listen to their silly remarks: 'They are jealous because you have a ladder and sunshade on your toadstool.'

Inch agreed that he was probably

right, then feeling sleepy he sat down under his sunshade. While he slept, a ladybird bumped into the toadstool and he woke up, with a start.

The ladybird cried, 'P-l-e-a-s-e, don't be angry. I didn't mean to waken you.'

'I'm not angry,' whispered Inch. 'My name is Inch Elf, and I'm pleased to meet you.'

'My name is Lucy Ladybird.'

'Do you live in Buttercup Wood?' asked Inch.

'I haven't a home,' said Lucy Ladybird, rather sadly.

'You can live with me. There is plenty of room on my toadstool, so please stay,' pleaded Inch.

Lucy Ladybird joyfully agreed.

'Now I have two friends,' said Inch happily. Lucy soon made herself at home on the toadstool and helped to keep it clean and tidy.

Shipwreck

The children trudged across the burning sand on the beach. It was very hot and they were thirsty after their trek. Stephen was at the head of the line. Then there came Josie, his sister, and after her, Paul, their best friend. The beach was empty.

'We must find someone soon. I'm dying of thirst,' moaned Josie. The scorching sun was burning the back of her neck.

But Stephen didn't answer. He marched steadily on, holding on high the scrap of white sail that he had salvaged from the wreck. He was the leader – he must keep the others going.

Paul was looking longingly ahead to the outcrop of rock which they were to walk around to get to the next bay. Would there be someone there . . .?

'Come on, children, forget about your shipwrecks and have a cold drink,' called Mum from the beach shelter. 'I thought you'd never finish playing with that old raft round there on the next beach.'

Dragon soup

There was once a lonely dragon who lived in a cave. He grew bored with guarding his treasure, so one day he decided to travel the world.

On powerful wings he soared until he came to a great city. A delicious smell reached him. 'Mmmm!' sniffed the dragon, 'I shall investigate.' Down he flew and landed by a sign which read '*Dame Trip's Pie Shop*'.

The dragon entered the pie shop and was distressed to find Dame Trip weeping. She cried even louder when she saw a dragon in her shop.

'Don't cry,' said the dragon, 'I don't eat people!'

Dame Trip looked relieved. 'I'm in such a bother. The King is coming for dinner and my recipe book has been stolen.'

'My goodness,' said the dragon, 'may I help? I have a secret recipe for dragon soup.'

The King arrived and sat at the Royal Table. 'Where is my pie?' he shouted. 'Allow me,' said the dragon, 'to present Your Majesty with my special dragon soup.'

'Dragon soup?' said the King. He tasted it. 'Wonderful! Will you be my Royal Dragon?'

So there the dragon remained, and he was never lonely again.

Night and morning

The cockerel opened one sleepy eye and saw a golden circle in the sky.

'That must be the sun,' he thought, perching on the gate. 'Cock-a-doodle doo! It's morning!' he cried.

The hens wearily moved into the run to start scratching. 'What a dark day!' they said.

The cows moved slowly to the gate. 'The farmer is late fetching us this morning,' they said.

'Morning already?' whimpered the dog. He had spent a hard day rounding up the sheep and still felt tired.

A large white bird flew overhead.

'Who are you?' asked the cockerel.

'I'm an owl,' said the bird. 'Whatever are you all doing up in the middle of the night?'

'The cockerel crowed. It must be morning,' cried the animals, making such a noise that the owl clasped its wings over its ears.

'The sun is in the sky,' said the cockerel.

The owl hooted with laughter.

'That's not the sun. That's a big, round full moon.'

So they all went back to bed.

The cockerel decided to open both eyes and make sure that the sun really was the sun before crowing in future.

The sandcastle

Daniel and Jamie were twin brothers. Daniel had blue eyes and blonde hair, and was four years old. Jamie had blue eyes and blonde hair and was four years old, too.

One day their Mummy took them to the park, and the boys had fun running up the hill and down again.

'Look Danny, a sandpit,' cried Jamie.

'I like playing with sand,' said Danny. 'I can make a castle. Oh, but we didn't bring our buckets and spades.'

Mummy spread a tablecloth on the grass. 'Come and have tea,' she called. 'Egg sandwiches and chocolate cake.'

When they had finished tea, they thanked Mummy, and ran back to the sandpit.

'Take off your shoes and socks,' she called.

The boys started to build a castle.

'It would be better with my spade,' said Danny.

Mummy gave the boys a drink in paper cups.

'I have an idea,' said Danny. 'My cup is like a bucket, I will put sandpies all around the castle.'

'I wish I had a flag for the top,' said Jamie.

'I've got the very thing,' said Mummy, who had been listening. And she gave him a small paper handkerchief tied to an ice lolly stick.

'What a splendid castle!' they all said when it was finished.

The fair

Every year in the village a fair was held. James always went with his mother, and for weeks before he saved all his money to spend there.

The day arrived once more and James gazed down the street at the roundabout, the coconut shy and the stalls selling hot dogs and candy floss.

But the most intriguing of all was a stall full of fish bowls. People were trying to land ping-pong balls inside them, and the prizes were tiny goldfish.

James darted over, bought some balls and began to join in. His money had nearly run out when at last he had some luck.

Mother said, 'Well done, James! Let's see if we can win another fish to keep that one company.'

Mother was lucky, too, and the fair lady handed James the two fish in a bag of water. On the way home they stopped to buy a goldfish bowl.

'Next year,' said James, 'perhaps we'll win some more.'

Mother laughed, 'If we do, we'll have to buy them a bigger bowl.'

Little dog

Mary had a little dog;
She wished it would obey,
But everywhere that Mary went,
It went the other way!

Dinnertime

Once there were three ducks who lived on a pond. One day they heard a rustling noise in the bushes and they were afraid.

'A fox! A fox!' they cried. 'He will eat us up for his dinner.'

Brown Duck flew to the edge of the pond and sat in the mud where she couldn't be seen.

Green Duck flew away into the long grass. He knew that the grass hid his green feathers.

They both forgot all about little White Duck. She was so afraid that she didn't know what to do, so, she stayed right where she was, in the middle of the blue pond. She was sure Mr Fox would catch her.

Then, out of the bushes and along the path came a little boy rustling a paper bag.

'Look, Mummy. What a lovely white duck!' said the little boy. 'Can I feed her?'

He threw some crusty bread out of his paper bag. Brown Duck and Green Duck watched from their hiding-places. They saw the fox slinking away and little White Duck enjoying her dinner, and they felt very hungry!

Christmas with Jolly

In winter time, Jolly the carthorse was kept warm in a stable.

On Christmas Eve Morning, the snow crunched under Peter's feet as he walked down there to see his friend.

'Hello Peter,' said Mr Barnaby, the farmer who owned Jolly. 'Tonight, we are going to harness Jolly.'

'At night?' said Peter, astonished.

Mr Barnaby grinned. 'Surprise job!'

Peter wondered all day what it could be. He could hardly wait.

At night, the air was tingling with Christmas.

They harnessed Jolly and then, as they backed him into the shafts of the big cart, people began arriving.

'We are going carolling,' laughed Mr Barnaby, and they all piled into the cart, with a load of lanterns.

Jolly snorted happily, and pulled them along the snowy roads.

'Merry Christmas!' people shouted to them. They stopped on the village green for everyone to join in the singing.

It was the best Christmas Eve Peter had ever known.

Afterwards, they took everyone home, and Peter rode on Jolly's back.

At Peter's house, Peter hugged him. 'Merry Christmas, Jolly,' he said, sleepily.

Pipkin and the spilt paint

Pixie Pipkin was buying some paint in the Fairyland Stores. 'I'll have a large pot of yellow paint for the outside of my house,' he said. 'And a large pot of pink paint for the inside.'

Pipkin hurried out of the shop. 'It's getting late,' he said to his friend, Silver-wing the Dove. 'I must hurry home before the sun sets.'

'I'll give you a ride home,' said Silver-wing. 'Jump on my back.'

Can you guess?

I'm red and high and rather wide.
I've room for seats and stairs inside.
Through countryside, and towns as
*   well,*
And stopping when I hear my bell,
I'll travel all day long.
What am I?

So Pipkin climbed on Silverwing's back and held his paint pots very carefully. Silverwing spread his wings and flew high into the sky. But Pipkin wasn't holding on tightly enough. 'Help, I'm slipping,' he gasped. He grabbed at Silverwing's feathers to save himself and the pots of paint slipped right out of his hands.

As they fell, the lids flew off, and pink and gold paint splashed all over the sky. 'Oh, dear,' cried Pipkin. 'Here comes Father Sun. Now I shall get into trouble.'

Everyone in Fairyland was looking up at the sky. 'What a beautiful sunset!' they all cried. Father Sun was so pleased that now he often asks Pipkin to paint him a special, sunset sky.

Hide and seek

Fluff and Sam were playing hide-and-seek, when Mrs Cat came back with the shopping. She put her basket down and went to make the kittens' tea.

It was Sam's turn to hide and when Fluff had counted to ten she started to look for him.

He wasn't under the stairs. He wasn't in the cupboard. He wasn't under the table. She couldn't find him anywhere.

Mrs Cat came in with the tea and joined in the search. They looked everywhere, but they couldn't find Sam.

'Well,' said Mrs Cat. 'I'll put the shopping away and then we'll have our tea. We've got lovely cream buns today.'

She picked up the basket of shopping.

'OH,' she squealed, as Sam sprang out of the basket. 'I didn't think you'd be far away at tea-time,' she laughed. 'But you did make me jump!'

121

Penny plays a tune

One day, when Penny was staying at Gran's, she heard someone playing the piano in the front room: Plink, plonk, plank – plank, plunk . . .

But when Penny looked, there was no one there! Then, she heard it again: Plink, plonk, plank, plinkle . . .

So she had another look. And still, no one was there!

'It must be someone,' said Penny.

So she crept back to the front room door and POUNCED in. But there was nobody – not even behind the chairs.

So Penny stood and played a tune on Gran's piano herself, with lots and lots of plinkles and plonkles.

Then, slowly . . . the curtain on the window ledge started to move, and out strolled Gran's ginger cat, Tango. He jumped on the piano and walked across the piano keys: Plink, plonk, plank!

'You'll *never* be as good on the piano as I am,' laughed Penny as she played a lot more plinkles and plonkles.

And it sounded so beautiful that Tango went fast asleep . . .

The crocodile

The crocodile has lots of teeth,
Some on the top
And some beneath.

He wades about the riverside
In search of food for his inside,
And through the water quickly hurtles
Eating fish and tiny turtles.

But what he really likes for tea
Is people . . . just like you and me!

Lucy Bodkin and the spring cleaning

'I shall do some spring cleaning!' declared Lucy Bodkin when she saw bright sunbeams shining into the dusty corners of her little house. Then out she went to the shops to buy everything she would need to make her home really clean and sparkling again.

On the way back that funny little lady was quite loaded up with broom, mop, scrubbing brush, bucket and feather duster – so she decided to rest under a shady tree. She put down all her cleaning things, except the feather duster which she used to flick away the flies and midges that buzzed around her in a most annoying way.

'SHOO! SHOO!' she cried, but in the end she could not put up with them a moment longer. She got up and went on her way carrying the feather duster – which she stuck in a vase as soon as she arrived home.

Then she sat in her favourite chair and looked around her room. How pretty it all

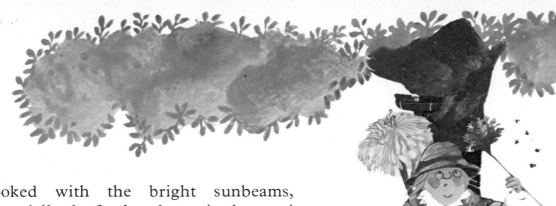

looked with the bright sunbeams, especially the feather duster in the vase!

'It's just like a lovely big feathery flower,' she thought sleepily.

By now the funny little lady had forgotten her spring cleaning. And the broom, mop, scrubbing brush and bucket she had left under a shady tree. Perhaps they are still there. Who knows?

I'm a picture on the wall

Another rainy day!

Robert sat glumly in his room. He looked around for something to do. He'd read all his books. He'd played with all his toys.

Then his eyes lit on the wall picture – a sailing ship cutting through foaming waves. Robert got up to look closer. There was no artist's name on it. He turned the picture over. There was writing on the back. It read:

I'm a picture on the wall,
With sea so blue and ship so tall.
You can change me in a thrice.
Just make a wish but say it twice.

Doubtfully, Robert mumbled a wish twice then turned the picture back.

The ship was gone. In its place was a castle with flags flying.

Robert made another wish. The castle faded. Now a spaceman landed on Mars. This was exciting. Scene after scene flashed by as Robert wished. Then the door opened.

'Bored, son?' his mother asked, looking in. 'Care to go to the cinema?'

'No, mother,' Robert answered quickly, 'I'm happy here.'

'Well,' mother murmured to herself closing the door, 'how he amuses himself with all those old toys and books, I'll never know!'

The stubborn house painter

No one knew why he did it, but he did. *He painted everything blue.* It wasn't that the stubborn house painter didn't know about other colours. Of course he did. He could talk of red, green and yellow, of vermilion, indigo and deep purple as well as you or I.

But he never used those colours. Why, he never so much as dipped his brush in them!

And it didn't matter if you begged him on bended knee to paint your house yellow-green or a beautiful, beautiful pink. When the job was finished it was always blue – deep blue, light blue, medium blue – but always blue.

And the funny thing about it was that blue looked best. 'Blue was the colour of the sky,' he said. 'Blue was the colour of the sea,' he smiled. 'Why, you just couldn't go wrong with blue,' he added.

So one of these days, look for a town that's all blue – houses and factories and smokestacks and shops, all blue.

Look for the stubborn house painter too. He's easy to spot. He wears a brilliant orange smock and a bright orange tie.

Strange, isn't it, for a man that loves blue.

The fat hippo

Hippo lived near a river. He ate weeds from its bottom and plants from its shore. How fat he grew! His stomach was like a barrel and he had ten chins.

But he was happy. He sang to the birds, he joked with the animals, he was the most popular creature around.

Then it happened. He saw himself in the river!

'Who's that fatty?' he cried.

'You!' the birds and animals laughed.

The Man in the Moon

The Man in the Moon lives high in the
sky,
Up and away where the clouds blow by –
And the Man in the Moon is remarkably
shy!
Haven't you noticed? He comes out to
play
Long after dusk at the end of the day,
And he only stays out while the sun is
away.
Then just before dawn when the sky
becomes light,
That shy little Man in the Moon takes
fright,
And hurries to hide 'til the following
night.

'I don't like me,' the hippo sniffed.

And he began to diet. He grew thinner and thinner. He stopped singing. He gave up joking. He was so grouchy he was the most unpopular creature around.

'Where are all my friends?' he suddenly cried one day.

'Gone,' a bird chirped, 'and I'm going too. We don't like thin, grumpy hippos.'

'Thin, grumpy hippos!' hippo muttered. 'I'll change that.' So, he began to eat and eat and eat.

He ate until his stomach was like a barrel. He ate until his ten chins returned. Then he began to sing and joke. Soon it was like old times with all the birds and animals around him.

But it wasn't quite the same. Hippo *never* looked in that river again. Can you guess why?

125

The chocolate cake

'Wait for me, while I'm in the Electricity Showrooms paying the bill,' said Pam and Peter's Mum.

'I like toy shops best,' said Peter.

'And cake shops,' said Pam. 'Let's play house while we're waiting.'

So they hid behind the fridges and electric cookers.

'What's for tea, love?' said Peter, pretending to be Dad.

'Chocolate sponge cake,' said Pam, 'with a silver rabbit on top.'

'Where is it then?'

'In the fridge,' said Pam.

'Get it out,' said Peter excitedly.

'Not until I've baked some more cakes,' said Pam.

Then, suddenly, Peter saw a tray of little cakes on a big new shiny cooker. 'There are some here,' he shouted, and he picked one up.

'They're toy ones,' called Pam.

'Put that cake down!' said Mum as they hurried out of the Showrooms.

'I wish that chocolate cake had been real,' said Peter as Mum went into the bread shop. 'I was really looking forward to eating a big piece of chocolate sponge.' Pam and Peter looked longingly at all the cakes in the bread shop window.

Just then, Mum came out of the shop and gave them a bag with two chocolate buns inside.

'They're just like the one with the silver rabbit on,' said Peter, smiling.

Pam nodded. She couldn't speak because her mouth was too full . . .

Football match

The football team
Have lost the ball.
Did Harry kick it to the wall?
The football nets have vanished too.
And now they don't know what to do!
The referee's whistle's
Slipped away . . .
Let's find them all
And start to play.

The pixie postman

Popper the pixie postman was feeling tired. His sack of letters seemed to be much heavier than usual. At last he saw a little dell and sat down on the grass to have a rest.

Soon his head began to nod and he fell fast asleep under a hazel tree. Then a little breeze began to blow and the hazel catkins started to swing on the branches. The yellow pollen from the catkins fell all over Popper's face.

Then Popper woke up and when he went to a pond to have a drink he saw his face in the water. It was yellow all over.

'Goodness, this must be a magic place!' cried Popper. He bent over a bit further to take a closer look at himself and fell into the pond with a big *splash*. He was soaked from head to toe.

The water washed all the yellow pollen from Popper's face, but he didn't stop to see that. He scrambled out of the pond and rushed off to deliver the rest of his letters very quickly.

When he reached home he peeped into the mirror and saw that his face was the right colour again. 'That really must have been a magic dell,' he said. 'I will never stop there again.'

He never did, and now all the letters get delivered on time.

The Wool-Bird

Once there was a Wool-Bird. He lived on a red calico cushion-cover. The Wool-Bird was yellow with green eyes. The calico cushion-cover was on the sofa in the sitting-room of Mrs Mirabelle Smee.

The Wool-Bird didn't like living on a calico cushion-cover.

He did not like the cushion.

He did not like the sofa.

He did not like the sitting-room.

And he did not like Mrs Mirabelle Smee.

Mrs Smee would often take up the cushion, fluff it and plump it, shake it and hit it, and then throw it back on to the sofa.

It made the Wool-Bird feel giddy. He just loathed being shaken about all over the place.

One thing he did like, however, was sitting on the balcony outside the sitting-room. Here he could watch the clouds form into white shapes of galloping horses, wandering sheep, and trampling elephants. It was fun.

The Wool-Bird would pretend that he was a real bird, that he could fly off and up and away, singing a gay song, into the sky among the horses, the sheep and the elephant-clouds.

One day, while Mrs Smee was in her kitchen preparing some coffee for her mid-morning snack, the Wool-Bird on the balcony-chair was wishing harder than he had ever wished before.

'I wish . . . I WISH . . .' wished the Wool-Bird.

'What do you wish?' asked a voice.

The Wool-Bird blinked and stared. Before him on the balcony stood a funny little man with red fuzzy hair and a red fuzzy beard.

'I,' said the little man importantly, 'am the Wishmonger and I'm here to help you.'

'Oh?' said the Wool-Bird doubtfully, not quite believing.

'Yes,' answered the Wishmonger firmly. Then he added, 'I was sitting in my house on top of the Wishing-Rock when you wished so hard that it began to sway from side to side as if in a hurricane. It always rocks like this when somebody wishes very, very, VERY hard for something.'

'What is your wish?' asked the Wishmonger.

'To be a REAL bird. To fly to the sky. Higher-than-high. To sing as I fly! Ooooooooooh!' and he gave a sigh of sheer delight at the thought of it.

'Is that all?' asked the Wishmonger.

'All?' exclaimed the Wool-Bird. 'All? Why, it's EVERYTHING.'

'Well, if that is all you want, it's easy,' the Wishmonger told him, and he muttered into his red beard.

The Wool-Bird began to feel a little bit peculiar. He felt a little bit warmer than usual. His two little claws seemed to be making a flickering movement. His tail felt a little bit twitchy. His eyes felt a little bit blinky. His wings felt a little bit fluttery.

'Well, Wool-Bird,' said the Wishmonger, 'it's happening. You are turning into a real bird. Soon you will be free of your calico-cushion, free to fly wherever you wish, to sing whenever you wish. . .'

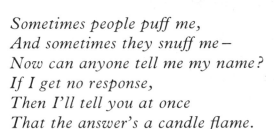

Riddle

Sometimes people puff me,
And sometimes they snuff me—
Now can anyone tell me my name?
If I get no response,
Then I'll tell you at once
That the answer's a candle flame.

And with these words the Wishmonger disappeared as suddenly and as mysteriously as he had come.

Mrs Smee came out on to the balcony carrying her tray of coffee.

Before she could sit down, the Wool-Bird wished—hard.

And then, to the amazement of Mrs Smee who dropped her tray with a crash, the Wool-Bird spread his wings and soared up over the balcony and away.

And he sang as he went: 'I'll never come back, I'll never come back, I'm a REAL bird now!'

A little mistake

Mitzi the witch was teaching her children how to make spells.

'Come now,' she said. 'You'll never become clever witches if you don't get the words right. That's better Jemima. Now I want you and Abigail to go into the forest, and cast a spell for me. You will see Prince Richard hunting there. He was very rude to me yesterday, and I want to teach him a lesson. After the magic words you say:

Eena Meena Mina Mog,
Change this prince into a dog.

and the dog will follow you home. Off you go.'

The children hid behind a tree until the prince came by. 'Now,' whispered Abigail. 'Say the magic spell.'

But to their horror, something went wrong. Prince Richard changed into a pig, and trotted away through the wood.

'Look what's happened,' gasped Abigail. 'You've turned him into a pig instead of a dog. Whatever will mother say?'

Mitzi was angry.

'But I didn't say pig,' cried Jemima.

'No, but you must have said hog, which is a kind of pig. Now we'll have to go and find him,' she said. 'If I want anything done properly, I always have to do it myself.'

The tail of Bossy Bunny

Bossy Bunny had the biggest, fluffiest tail in the warren.

'I am the most important bunny,' he would boast. 'I have the biggest tail.'

One day Bossy Bunny was playing with the other bunnies. Waving his big fluffy tail, he chased them under a gorse bush. There was just room for them to squeeze through.

A gorse bush has very pretty yellow flowers but lots of long thorns.

Bossy Bunny squeezed under the bush but could move no further. The thorns caught his fluffy tail and held him fast.

He did look funny. All the bunnies giggled.

'Stop laughing at me!' he cried. 'I am the most important bunny, as I have the biggest tail. Set me free at once.'

'We will have to cut the fur of your tail to free you,' said the bunnies.

'The fox will be out looking for bunnies soon,' sighed Bossy. 'You will have to cut my tail.'

So they did. It didn't hurt at all because it was only a bunch of fluffy fur.

Now Bossy is not an important bunny at all as he has the smallest tail in the warren, but he is much nicer.

Birthday surprise

Tommy's cake's in two bits on the
floor
Only three candles, but to-day he's
four.
But look, little Tommy, dry your eyes,
Your cake was upset by a birthday
surprise —
A puppy dog wagging his tail for joy
At being a gift for a fine little boy.

Alexander's elephant

One rainy Saturday afternoon, Alexander decided to play with his zoo. He set up all the cages and he found the zoo keeper carrying a bucket of fish for the sealions. Then he found his animals which were mixed up higgledy-piggledy in a box. That wouldn't do – they would be fighting in a moment! Quickly, Alexander put the animals in their right cages . . . lions, bears, tigers, giraffes, monkeys, zebras, crocodiles and the others. But where was his best elephant? It was nowhere to be found.

Alexander ran from the room and for fun he shouted, 'Help! A dangerous elephant has escaped from the zoo!'

Daddy said they must go out hunting straightaway. There was no time to lose.

'Raincoats and boots on!' he said.

Together they stalked around the garden in the rain, making their best animal-catching faces as they looked this way and that way.

'Sh-h-h,' whispered Daddy. 'It's in the shed.'

Alexander laughed to himself at the thought of a real enormous elephant squashed into a little garden shed.

'Got him!' cried Daddy opening the door and rushing in.

Sure enough there was Alexander's zoo elephant on the shelf where he had left it last week. Hunting for a dangerous escaped elephant had certainly been an exciting thing to do on a rainy Saturday afternoon.

Five funny balloons

John's red balloon sailed into the sky
Can you see it very high?

Lucy's balloon, yellow and gay,
Bounced down the road and far away.

David's balloon, round and green,
Has the funniest face you've ever seen.

Sarah's balloon, orange and bright,
Has magic stars that shine at night.

Nicky's balloon jumped hop-hop-hop
On a prickly hedgehog, and it burst,
POP! POP!

The Princess's party

The princess had a baby dragon who was very playful, breathing out flames everywhere. On her birthday he was in trouble with the princess for he had set light to the birthday candles long before the cake was ready to be eaten.

The princess took the dragon for a walk in the palace gardens, and whispered something to the gardener.

Before long the dragon couldn't resist making a tiny puff at a rose bush but the gardener acted quickly. Hidden behind the bushes, he turned on a big water spray which put out the flames and splashed all over the dragon.

'You're a naughty baby dragon,' said the princess, drying him with a towel. 'You must behave yourself at my bonfire party tonight.'

At the party, the gardener asked the dragon for his help. 'My matches are soaking wet from the spray,' he said. 'I can't light the bonfire or the fireworks.'

Fireworks! The dragon huffed and puffed with excitement and soon the bonfire was roaring away, with fireworks shooting in all directions.

And the princess felt very proud of her baby dragon.

Midsummer Night

'Not asleep yet Jane?' said her mother.

'Oh Mummy, it's a lovely night. Look at the stars.'

'Yes, it's Midsummer Night. Some call it fairy time.'

'Fairy time!' cried Jane. 'I wish I could see the fairies.'

And as she lay gazing at the stars a strange thing happened. They seemed to move and Jane saw they weren't stars any more, but fairies. They floated in through the window and Jane felt herself being lifted up, out into the moonlight.

One lovely fairy came to welcome her. 'We are the Midsummer fairies,' she said. 'On this night, we invite a child to our party to be our queen. Come, sit on the high seat.' And she put a crown of golden rosebuds on Jane's head.

It was a lovely party, but all too soon daylight came. The music and dancing stopped, and Jane was lifted gently back to bed.

'Wake up dear,' said Mummy the next morning.

'Oh Mummy, I was a queen last night.'

'Were you dear? But what's this? A flower caught in your hair?'

'Yes Mummy,' said Jane. 'That's one of the rosebuds from my fairy crown.'

The Greedy Dragon

Once there was a Greedy Dragon.

He liked to eat cheese and tomatoes, chocolates and candies, toffees and jellies, peaches and cream, bananas and custard, bad little boys and good little girls.

One day, a bad little boy named Bill went to visit the Greedy Dragon.

They stared at each other.

The Greedy Dragon puffed a puff-of-flame at Bill.

Bill put out his tongue at the Greedy Dragon.

'I'll eat you all up,' snarled the Greedy Dragon.

Bill just laughed at this. 'Huh! you greedy old Dragon,' he mocked. 'If you eat ME, I will give you the worst stomach-ache you ever had. The worst stomach-ache in the world.'

'Oho? You will, will you? Well, I say you won't. I say that I'll eat you if I like. And,' the Greedy Dragon added, licking his scaly lips, 'I do like.'

How many?

*How many eggs
In a cuckoo's nest?
How many feathers
On a bee?
How many stars
In the midnight sky?
How many leaves
On a tree?*

*If you can guess
Nod your head for YES.*

And with these words he ran towards Bill and, because he was such a greedy Dragon, he swallowed him whole. How surprised he was to hear Bill laughing all the way down! He wondered why. To be swallowed by a Dragon is no laughing matter, he thought. He scratched his long nose with his claw. 'Very odd,' he said to himself. 'Very puzzling. What has

'My tummy! My poor tummy!'

And he stopped scratching his nose to hold his stomach in his two claws.

The little flicker from the two flints gave Bill just enough to see where to touch off the magic firework. He lit it.

The magic firework gave a tremendous ROAAARRR and, as the Greedy Dragon shrieked, 'Help! Fire! Water! Police!' it shot Bill up and out of the Dragon's wide-open mouth and onto a ledge safely out of his reach.

But the work of the magic firework was not yet done. Oh dear no! It zoomed around the Greedy Dragon's head. Seven times it circled about. At the seventh circling, the spell worked.

The great big Greedy Dragon turned into a tiny, green, harmless dragonfly which flew up and away into the sky.

And Bill? Well, Bill just laughed to himself all the way home.

he got to laugh about for goodness sake?' He very soon found out.

Bill had a magic firework and two magic stones in his pocket. (He always filled his pockets with bits-and-pieces of magic stuff.)

Bill rubbed the two stones together. This rubbing produced a tiny little flame which, small though it was, caused the Greedy Dragon to cry out:

The knitted doll

Amanda had a woolly doll with long knitted legs, and knitted clothes in pink, green and yellow stripes.

One day, they went to the park. 'Sit here,' said Mummy, 'and wait.' So Amanda sat on a park seat, and the knitted doll sat beside her. They watched the ducks together.

Mummy came back with such a big icecream that Amanda had to hold it with both hands! When they set off for their walk around the park, they forgot the knitted doll and it had gone by the time they got back.

An old, old man, was sitting on the next seat. 'Have you seen a knitted doll?' Mummy asked him. The old man pointed with his stick. 'That little dog has just taken it,' he said.

Amanda gasped. For there was a puppy, scattering the ducks and shaking a bundle of pink, green and yellow stripes. Amanda ran after him and as the puppy turned, she managed to grab a long, woolly leg. 'My Dolly!' she yelled.

'My puppy!' yelled another voice, as the puppy merrily tugged and tugged. He thought it great fun.

But his owner stopped the game, and rescued the doll.

Amanda was very careful not to leave her knitted doll anywhere again!

The Wind blew himself down to a breeze while Kiku fetched some paper and wood and began to make a kite. He painted a big, red dragon on it and made a long tail with strips of green and gold. When he threw it into the air the Wind caught it and whisked it away, over land and sea, and soon he was back at Tommy's house.

Tommy had been allowed to get up and he was just coming out into the garden. The Wind dropped the kite down at Tommy's feet. 'Gosh,' cried Tommy, grabbing the long string. 'What a super kite!'

The Wind played with Tommy and the kite all afternoon, until Tommy felt well again. 'I don't think I've been naughty, after all,' said the Wind. 'In fact I think I've been quite good.'

Tommy's kite

'*Whoo-hoo*!' cried the Wind, 'I feel like being naughty today.' He blew bits of paper along the street and rattled at Tommy's bedroom window.

Tommy was in bed because he hadn't been well. 'That boy needs cheering up,' said the Wind. So he blew himself away, over land and sea, to the land of the rising sun where Kiku the kite-maker lived.

Kiku came running out of his house. 'Be careful, please,' he said, bowing low. 'Last time honourable Wind blew roof off house.'

A heavy load home

Father, Mother and the twins were on vacation. Their little car easily overtook lorries as it sped towards the seacoast and soon they were at their hotel.

The days were spent on the sunny beaches. The twins waded around tidal pools, among the coloured rocks and driftwood. Mother and Father lay in the sun.

Then vacation was over. They drove back over the moors. When they stopped to picnic the twins climbed over the moss-covered rocks.

Back in the car they headed towards the hills of home. They sped along smoothly, passing great lorries. But, at the first hill the car slowed down. Father shifted into lower gear. The car went even slower. Now the lorries were passing them.

Father stopped the car at a lay-by. He jumped out and opened the bonnet. 'Everything's all right here,' he said. He scratched his head. Then he opened the boot. 'Look here, Mother,' he laughed.

Mother looked in. A great pile of coloured rocks and driftwood covered their suitcases. Moss-covered stones lay everywhere.

The twins just sat in the car staring straight ahead. They didn't say a word.

But their faces were beet-red.

Santa's secret present

They start in train as well as in car,
Then in doll but not in star,
In a ball but not in bat,
In an owl but not in cat,
In pencils too, but not in chalks,
And in running but not in walks.

Next in swimming – not in lake,
Then in king-pins and in cake.
In apples – yes – but not in plums
In toffees too but not wine gums.
Then in present – not in gift
In stockings – or trousers . . .
They make your feet swift!
What are they in two words?

The May Day mug

Everyone knows that from May Eve through May Day is a magic time when everybody has to be extra careful and keep out of fairy rings and away from witches' ditches.

One May morning, Roger had a whole pound to spend and he knew exactly what he was going to buy – a mug. He had seen it in a dusty old shop window. It was green with a red imp painted on it. Roger went into the shop and asked the old man behind the counter: 'The green mug with the red imp, please.'

'Are you sure?' asked the shopkeeper in a strange quivery-quavery voice.

'Certain-sure,' Roger replied.

He handed over his pound-note and took the green mug home and filled it with milk. The doorbell rang. Roger opened the door. There was no-one there, so he went back to the kitchen. His mug was where he had left it but there was not a drip of milk in it.

'That's odd,' said Roger, and poured more milk into the mug. He raised it to his lips. The doorbell rang again. He put down the mug, went to the door and . . . there was no one there. He returned and found the mug empty again. This happened *seven* times. Imagine!

And then – Roger heard a dozen squeaky little voices singing:

'Hahaha! Hohoho!
May Day's a magic day –
Or didn't you know?
Your mug was made in Pixieland,
Tricksyland, Pixieland,
Made by the Pixie-Tricksy-Men.'

And it was not until May Day was over that Roger was able to drink his milk from the green mug with the red imp picture on it.

139

Scamp

Bess the Sheepdog was a great help to Farmer Biggs. Her puppy, Scamp, was no help at all. He followed Bess everywhere and got in the way and frightened the sheep.

'Go home, Scamp,' Bess scolded.

'But I want to help,' said Scamp.

Bess gave him a push. 'You're much too young,' she said.

So Scamp wandered off. But he hadn't gone far when he saw a lamb caught in the brambles, so he dived into the hedge and tore at the thorny branches with his teeth.

'Ouch,' he yelped, as the thorns scratched his nose.

'Baa-aa,' cried the lamb.

When he had the lamb free from the hedge, he chased her back to the pen, just like Bess would have done.

Farmer Biggs was very pleased with him for bringing the lamb back safely. 'That puppy is going to make a fine sheepdog one day,' he said to Bess.

Scamp was very proud, but he rubbed his sore nose and thought he'd wait until he was bigger.

The happy home for old horses

A rocking-horse stood in an attic. His paint was chipped and his mane and tail thin, but his eyes were bright. His hooves still longed to break into a rocking canter. Once everyone in the nursery had loved him. Now he was forgotten.

A man buying second-hand things passed by ringing his bell, and soon the rocking-horse was in the back of a van.

The next stop was by a big gateway. Surprised, the rocking-horse read a notice: HAPPY HOME FOR OLD HORSES. He thrilled with excitement! Wriggling cautiously, he managed to topple out of the van onto the road and set off towards the gate. A man standing there grabbed his rein.

The van-driver strode up. 'Hey, that's *my* horse!'

'He'll be mine when I've paid for him,' replied the other man. 'He's come to the right place.'

And he had. For although the rocking-horse spent each night indoors, he stood at the field gate during the day and chatted with the other old horses.

Rachel's runaway kitten

Rachel's Mummy had asked the sweep to come and clean the empty chimney. He arrived with lots of big clattering brushes.

Rachel's new tabby kitten, Henry, didn't like the noisy sweep, so he scampered away and hid.

'I must find Henry,' said Rachel. 'He'll be frightened.'

She looked under the chairs and behind the curtains but there was no sign of Henry Kitten.

'Let's look for him in the garden,' suggested Mummy.

They called Henry and put a saucer of milk down for him, but still the kitten didn't appear.

'Oh, look,' said Mummy. 'There's the sweep's brush coming out of the chimney . . . and there's Henry coming out of the chimney too!'

'That's not Henry,' said Rachel. 'Henry's a tabby kitten, not a black one.'

'That's because he's all covered in soot,' laughed Mummy.

The sweep fetched a ladder. He lifted Henry down from the roof, and put him into Rachel's arms.

Henry purred with happiness. Then he drank his milk, purred again, and licked his fur clean until all his tabby stripes were showing once more.

The Fairy and the bulldozer

Deep within a wood lived the Bluebell Fairy. Early one morning she heard a terrible noise: 'Brrrum, brrum-brrum,' it went. The Bluebell Fairy hurried to find out what it could be. A big yellow bulldozer had come to make a road through her wood.

'Please stop!' cried the Fairy. 'You will kill my bluebell flowers.'

But the man who was driving the bulldozer didn't hear her. 'Brrrum,' went the engine loudly, and the big wheels rumbled towards the bluebell patch.

Then, suddenly, a Good Thought came into the man's head. 'What a shame,' said the Thought, 'to spoil those lovely bluebells. Why not move them to a place far away from the road where they won't be hurt?'

So the man climbed down from the bulldozer. Carefully, he lifted the bluebells out of the soil. Carefully, he carried them deep into the wood. And carefully, he planted them again.

Then he started up his yellow bulldozer and began to clatter and clank through the wood. And the Good Thought that had come into his head flew away and changed back into the Bluebell Fairy.

The tweed coat

'How dreadful to be sent to a jumble sale!' said the fur coat.

A pink satin dress shuddered, her frills fluttering anxiously. 'We will be put in heaps with quite shabby clothes and sold cheaply. So insulting for expensive clothes like us!'

A slim tweed coat was longing to escape and hoped somebody young would buy her, but an old lady took her home.

'I'm sure I can make it fit,' said the old lady, picking up her scissors. And she snipped and stitched until bedtime. When she had finished the old lady hung the jacket up carefully.

Next day, a little girl came to stay. 'Holly, come and meet Apple,' said her granny.

In the orchard was a little grey pony!

Then Granny showed Holly the tweed coat, which she had turned into a riding jacket for her. It fitted her perfectly.

What fun Holly and Apple had! And so did the tweed jacket.

Miss Fish and Miss Mermaid

Hello, Miss Fish,
Come out to play?

Oh no, Miss Mermaid,
Not today.

Why not, Miss Fish?
Please tell me why?

I'm busy making
A seaweed pie.

A close shave

Fanny Fieldmouse loved Alexander the best of all her family, but there was one thing that worried her. He was so disobedient.

One day she said, 'Alexander, don't go into the cornfield. The corn is being cut, and it's very dangerous.'

But Alexander took no notice. 'I'll be all right,' he thought. 'That cutting machine is a long way off. Why, here's our old nest! It's rather breezy up here, so I'll tie my tail to this grass stalk and curl up for a nap.' Soon he was fast asleep.

Suddenly, a fearful noise woke him, and now he could see that only a little corn was left uncut, and the dreadful blades of the machine were coming closer. He tried to undo the knot in his tail, but his little paws were cramped.

Now the knives were almost overhead. Suddenly, BUMP, he landed on the ground, and a voice gasped: 'Run for your life.'

Alexander shot off, just as the blades sliced off nearly all his whiskers. Bobtail Bunny had nibbled through the stalk just in time!

The new tractor

Simon lived in the country. His daddy had bought a farm. It was all very different from living in a town and Simon loved every minute.

On Saturday morning Simon and his daddy were up even earlier than usual. They had to do all their morning jobs as quickly as possible – because it was the day the new tractor was going to be delivered.

His father had just finished cleaning out the cowshed when he heard Simon call out in delight, 'Daddy, it's coming! Come on, let's go to the gate.'

Simon's daddy was just as excited as Simon. They opened the gate and cheered as the tractor pulled into the farmyard.

The delivery man laughed at them and jumped down. 'Well, Mr King – she's all yours now, and here are the keys, young man,' he smiled, handing them to Simon.

'Oh, Daddy, can we have a ride straightaway?' asked Simon.

'Just try and stop me!' laughed his daddy – and soon they were both seated high on the new tractor as they took it for a spin round the farmyard.

Sammy to the rescue

Sammy the engine was very cross. 'I'm tired of shunting up and down this line. Nothing exciting happens. I wish I could take passengers to town like Herbert.'

'Now Sam,' said Ben his driver. 'We're very lucky this line is still open. Come along, we have work to do.'

So off they went, and in the distance they saw a number of people waving to them to stop.

'Look! there's Farmer Joe,' said Ben. 'I wonder what's wrong.'

'Oh Ben,' said Joe. 'My cow Belinda has fallen into the pond. The fire brigade promised to help, but they've been called away, and Belinda is getting cold. We've put a rope round her, and if we tie the other end to your engine, could you help us pull her out?'

'I'm sure we can,' said Ben. So when they were ready, he drove Sam forward very carefully. Everyone pulled and soon Belinda was out safely.

'Well done, Ben and Sammy,' said Joe. 'We could use a little engine like you, when we open the old Cowslip Line. Would you like to take the passengers to the seaside every weekend?'

'What do you say Sam?' said Ben.

'Toot! Toot!' hooted Sammy the engine joyfully.

The unhappy apple

Once there was an Apple who lived all alone in the Land of the Oranges. He was very unhappy, because the Oranges made fun of him.

'Why are you so green and hard?' they would ask. 'Why aren't you soft and juicy like us?'

Apple didn't know why. And he left the Land of the Oranges to journey through the world in search of other Apples like himself.

After many long days he came to a beautiful country. It was full of trees, and each tree was covered with pink flowers. Apple decided to rest there for a while.

Then a magic thing happened. As he watched, the flowers on the trees began to change. Their colour turned from pink to green, and they grew big and round and hung down from the branches.

Suddenly one of them dropped to the ground – PLOP – right beside Apple.

'Why!' he cried in astonishment. 'You look exactly like me!'

'Of course I do,' came the answer. 'I'm a new Apple. This is the Apple Tree Orchard where all the Apples in our land grow. Why don't you stay here with us?'

And Apple did, and he was never lonely or unhappy again.

Sam's chimney brush

Sam the chimney-sweep was too dirty to go to the party.

'How do you sweep chimneys?' asked Witch Winnie who thought Sam's job must be very unpleasant.

Sam showed Witch Winnie his brush and all the wooden poles that fitted together to make a handle long enough to go up the tallest chimney.

That day it rained. It went on raining until it had washed all the soot from Sam's clothes and his hair. Water ran down the street. No-one could get to the party.

'Take people on your broomstick,' said Sam.

'I could only take one at a time,' said Winnie. 'Your brush would be long enough for everyone.'

So Sam joined all the handles together to make a very long brush. Witch Winnie said a few magic words and Sam sat on the brush and flew it through the village.

'All aboard!' he cried, and everyone jumped on to his magic chimney brush.

It was a lovely party.

Sam never swept chimneys again. He set up a flying chimney brush service instead.

The tree

I am a tall tree
And my roots are so strong,
My branches stretch out
For the birds to sit on.

My leaves rustle softly
And drink in the light
Which makes me grow wider
And helps me gain height.

There's a hole in my middle
Round, cosy and deep
Where a little brown owl lives
All day, fast asleep.

The adventures of Stanley

Stanley was a ginger cat who lived inside a dustbin down an alley near the docks. Stanley loved to watch the ships unload, especially when sailors threw him scraps of fish.

One morning Stanley had an idea. 'I shall go to sea,' he thought, 'I shall be a ship's cat!'

Off he marched towards a ship called *Jolly Jack*. 'This is the life,' yawned Stanley. He stretched out on a sack and went to sleep.

Stanley awoke with a shock. 'Oooh! What's happening?' He was soaked with water. The ship tossed and rolled over the waves. Thunder boomed!

'Ah! A stowaway!' said the ship's captain. He picked up seasick Stanley and carried him below.

After two helpings of bully beef and a jug of cream, Stanley felt much better. The storm had cleared, the sea was calm. The crew sang sea shanties on deck, and Stanley danced the Hornpipe.

At the end of the day, Stanley waved goodbye and went back to his dustbin in the alley. 'Home, sweet home,' he sighed, and fell asleep.

Patrick's present

It was Patrick's birthday, and he had a 'phone call from his Aunty Phyl.

'I'm bringing you a present this afternoon, Patrick,' said Aunty. 'It's green, it looks fierce, and it flies.'

That was all Aunty would tell him, and Patrick was puzzled.

'Perhaps it's a green, fierce bird,' he told Mum. 'I'm not sure that I want a green, fierce bird for my birthday.'

At last, it was tea-time, and Aunty arrived. She handed Patrick a long, thin parcel.

'It must be a long, thin, green, fierce bird,' thought Patrick, and he opened the parcel slowly and carefully, in case anything long and thin and green and fierce should fly out at him.

When all the paper was off, Patrick gasped: *'It's a kite!'*

'You sound so surprised,' laughed Aunty Phyl. 'I wonder what you thought it was.'

Patrick unfolded the kite and, on the front of it, saw a picture of a very green, rather fierce dragon.

'So that was what Aunty was talking about,' said Patrick to his Mum.

He asked his Aunty if she would come out into the garden, and help him fly the kite. It was a windy afternoon, and the kite flew beautifully. That fierce, green dragon was soon high above the rooftops.

Polly the polar bear

Polly is a polar bear
Living in the coldest air,
Moving in the sparkling snow,
Watching Northern Lights aglow,
Swimming in the icy sea,
Catching fishes for her tea.
Because she's white
She's hardly seen;
Only paw marks show
She's been . . .

Charlie's champion ears

Peter thought Charlie was the best dog in the world. Charlie was a spaniel with long, floppy black ears – so long that when he took a drink of water, they hung down into the bowl and got all wet.

Peter liked taking Charlie for walks, except when they met Mr Rankin, who always patted Charlie and said, 'Hello, Big Ears!' Peter thought he was making fun of Charlie, so when they got home Peter hugged him and said, 'Never mind, Charlie – I *like* your ears!'

One Saturday, Peter and his parents, and Charlie, went to a dog show in the park, with competitions for The Most Obedient Dog, The Prettiest Dog . . . *and* The Dog with the Longest Ears. Charlie won that easily, and the judge gave Peter a little medal as a prize.

Next day, when Mr Rankin met them and said 'Hello, Big Ears!', Peter fingered the prize medal in his pocket, and this time he felt proud.

As they walked on, he bent down and patted Charlie, who wagged his tail and looked up at him. Peter couldn't be sure, but it seemed to him that Charlie actually winked at him.

Miss Little's new home

Miss Little was the smallest doll in the dolls' house, and everything there was too big for her. She couldn't sit on a chair, or get into bed without any of the bigger dolls helping her. Miss Dainty Doll and Mrs Raggedy were just the right size for the dolls' house, and lived there comfortably. But Miss Little, who couldn't reach shelves, cupboards, tables or the sink was not happy – at least, not until a new toy arrived in the playroom one day.

The new toy was a weather house from Switzerland. On fine days, a lady doll called Mrs Sun came out of the weather house, and on wet days, out came a man doll with an umbrella.

'Folk can tell what the weather will be when they look at the weather house,' said Mrs Sun.

She invited Miss Little inside, and Miss Little saw that the furniture was just her size.

When Mrs Sun heard Miss Little's problem, she said, 'Do come and live with us. We would like some company.'

Miss Little fetched her clothes, and moved in to the weather house.

'I'll visit Miss Dainty Doll and Mrs Raggedy every Sunday,' said Miss Little. 'For the rest of the time I shall live in the weather house. On wet days, when Mr Rain is out, I'll have Mrs Sun to talk to, and on fine days, when Mrs Sun is out, I'll talk to Mr Rain. How lucky I am!'

A Jolly good deed

Peter was keeping Jolly the carthorse company, when a young lady appeared on the lane. Her shoes were much too high for country walks. 'Oh dear!' she

Help the Fairy Queen reach her palace

Which road leads to the palace gate?
Although the Queen must not be late,
The fairy coachman cannot tell
Because a witch has cast a spell.
She's turned the signposts all around
So that the right way can't be found.
But with a pencil you can see
Which road will bring them home
for tea.

cried. 'Is there a garage near, please?'

'Yes,' said Peter, curiously, 'But it's not open today – it's Sunday!'

'Oh no!' she wailed, 'I have such a long way to go. What am I to do? My car is in a ditch. I skidded.'

'Wait here,' said Peter. 'I will fetch Jolly's owner,' and he gave her a carrot to give to Jolly.

She stared nervously at the enormous horse, but Jolly soon made friends with her.

Peter came hurrying back with Mr Barnaby. To her surprise they said, 'Jolly can help you.'

They walked Jolly to the stranded car. Mr Barnaby tied ropes on it, then fastened them onto the horse.

'Righto, Peter,' he called, pushing the car, and Peter urged Jolly forward.

Jolly strained every large limb, and the car, slowly rolled up the ditch, and onto the road.

The lady was overjoyed. 'What a wonderful horse!' she cried.

Next day, she sent a huge box marked: 'Especially for Jolly.' It was full of carrots!

Half a secret

'Can we go to see the Queen?' asked Lucy.

'One day soon, when we've bought you new shoes,' said Mummy, and they went to the shop to buy new shoes.

'Can we go now to see the Queen?' asked Lucy.

'One day soon when we've bought you a new hat and coat,' said Mummy, and they went to the shop to buy a new hat and coat.

'Can we go *now* and see the Queen?' pleaded Lucy, and her mother said, 'When I've finished my knitting.'

'What are you making?' said Lucy.

'Will you tell me or is it a secret?'

'It's half a secret,' said Mummy mysteriously, carefully knitting a shape striped in red, white and blue.

Soon the other half of the secret was finished and Mummy held up a red, white and blue pair of . . .

'. . . mittens, for me!' shouted Lucy in delight.

'*Now* we will go and see the Queen!' said Mummy, and they did.

Lucy cheered and waved her hands in their red, white and blue mittens when the Queen rode by in her golden coach.

And the Queen waved back!

Naughty kittens

Red, blue, green and yellow
Kitten is a naughty fellow —
He and his friends each gave a pull
And now they've tangled Mother's
wool.
Before she sees them all and scolds,
Find the wool
Each kitten holds.

Ted's toy shop

Ted the toy shop man was rather sad because a big, bright new supermarket had opened opposite his little shop, and he hadn't nearly as many customers as before.

He put a Jack-in-the-box in the front of his window for the children to see. Jack didn't know that the supermarket had a clock that struck nine o'clock, which was opening time, very noisily. When Jack first heard it he was so startled he jumped way up high and right out of his box!

He jumped so hard he hit a teddy bear who hit him back and made the fairy doll cry.

'Sssh . . . sssh . . .' whispered the train, but no one took any notice so it started clattering along its rails. It bumped into a ball which rolled into an aeroplane.

Zoom! The aeroplane flew round the toy shop, bursting a bunch of balloons and colliding with Ted's parrot which fell off its perch.

'Hullabaloo! Hullabaloo!' screamed the parrot and then Ted came through the shop to open up.

He couldn't believe his eyes, especially when he saw that outside the window was a big crowd of children who had come running to see the fun and to buy all his toys.

Lucy Bodkin and the lawn-mower

It was Lucy Bodkin's lawn mowing day but the very thought of pushing a heavy old lawn-mower up and down made poor Lucy feel extremely hot and tired. She decided to sit and look at the flowers instead. She liked the tall pink foxgloves growing wildly wherever they pleased, and the bright orange marigolds.

Suddenly, Lucy Bodkin heard a peculiar noise: *munch-munch-munch-munch.* She looked up . . . and what a surprise! A small white goat had wandered in and was munching hungrily at the long grass.

What a friendly little thing, thought Lucy! And so helpful.

'Would you like to eat all my grass?' she asked the goat.

'MA-A-A,' it replied as if it meant 'yes please.'

'Would you like to live here forever?' asked Lucy.

'MA-A-A,' replied the goat again, between mouthfuls of juicy grass.

'Well then,' said the funny little lady. 'I'll call you LORNA. It's a good name for a small goat who likes eating lawns.'

So Lorna stayed forever and Lucy Bodkin never had to cut her grass again.

The Robin's waistcoat

It was autumn in the wood, and the bare trees shivered in the wind.

'Winter will soon be here,' thought Robin. 'It's time I put on my warm red waistcoat.' He looked around his nest. But the waistcoat wasn't there.

'Where can it be?' he said. 'Oh dear, I shall catch such a cold if I don't find my red winter waistcoat.'

He flew through the wood searching for it. Could that be it, hanging from a holly bush? No, it was only a spray of scarlet holly berries.

Robin flew on. Then he saw something red on top of a log. It was the missing waistcoat – and huddled inside it was Sparrow!

'Why have you taken my waistcoat?' Robin asked crossly.

'Oh Robin, the wind is so cold. It blows right through my feathers,' said Sparrow in a sad little voice. 'I borrowed it to keep myself warm.'

Robin felt sorry for him. 'You can have my brown waistcoat,' he said. 'It's much too small for me. It will fit you nicely.'

And to this day, Sparrow still wears a brown waistcoat, and Robin always wears a red one.

Biscuits for tea

Martin and Mary and Mandy and me –
All of us like eating biscuits for tea.
Martin is greedy and gobbles up eight,
But Mary takes only two from the plate.
Mandy eats four; I have just one –
And that was the last one, so now
       they're all gone.
If you count up carefully, you'll find
       if you're clever
The number of biscuits we ate altogether.

Neil's new puppy

Neil had been given a new puppy – a little, fluffy fellow, who didn't yet have a name.

'I don't know what to call him,' said Neil to Daddy.

'Well,' said Daddy, 'he has just dug a big hole in my flower bed. How about calling him Digger?'

'I don't think I like that name, Daddy,' said Neil. 'I'm very sorry about the hole.'

'Mummy,' said Neil, 'I don't know what to call my puppy.'

'Well,' said Mummy, 'he has just chewed one of my slippers, and ripped it into shreds. How about calling him Ripper?'

'I don't think I like that name, Mummy,' said Neil. 'I'm very sorry about the slipper.'

Mummy and Daddy weren't really cross.

'When your puppy is a little older, he will stop being so naughty,' said Daddy.

'When he has calmed down a little, he will stop being such a scamp,' said Mummy.

'That's what I'll call him!' cried Neil, at once. 'SCAMP! Yes, Scamp shall be his name, because he is a Scamp, isn't he?'

Mary's little lamb

There was once a little white lamb who lived on a farm with a girl named Mary. And wherever Mary went, the lamb followed closely behind her.

But one day, Mary said, 'Tomorrow I'm going to school. Lambs aren't allowed there, so you must stay here on the farm until I come home.'

Next morning, Mary walked by herself down the lane to school. She sat at her desk in the classroom with the other children, and watched the teacher chalk pictures on the blackboard.

Suddenly, there came a funny little noise: 'baaa . . . baaa . . . atishoo!'

It was Mary's little white lamb! He had followed her to school, and hidden himself behind the blackboard. But the dust from the chalk had tickled his nose.

The teacher smiled. 'Well,' she said, 'lambs who come to school must be taught a lesson.'

So the little lamb had to sit at a desk. 'How uncomfortable it is!' he thought to himself.

Then the teacher gave him a book about history. 'How boring it is!' he thought.

To end the day, the class had a number lesson. 'It's much more fun back on the farm,' the little lamb decided.

And he never followed Mary to school again.

Have you seen . . .

A little blue bird,
A red-leaved tree,
A deep green river,
Turquoise sea;
Bright yellow fields,
Rose-pink skies,
An orange sun,
Or hazel eyes;
Purple hills,
A white stone wall;
Just look . . .
and you will see them all!

A to-do at the zoo

Not long ago, the keeper who feeds the animals at the zoo went on a holiday. A new keeper came to look after them. When it was dinner time, he gave the animals their food. But oh dear – the silly man got all the plates mixed up, and everyone was given the wrong dinner!

The elephant glared at his plate. 'I don't eat *fish*!' he squealed.

The sealion stared at his plate. 'I don't eat *chops*!' he honked.

The tiger scowled at his plate. 'I don't eat *nuts*!' he roared.

The monkey frowned at his plate. 'I don't eat *leaves*!' he shrieked.

All the animals were very cross. They made so much noise that the new keeper came running to see what was wrong.

'Oh, what a to-do,' he said. 'I can't remember who eats what. Will you help me?'

So the elephant gave the plate of fish to the sealion. And the sealion gave the plate of chops to the tiger. And the tiger gave the plate of nuts to the monkey. And the monkey gave the plate of leaves to the elephant.

Then they all gobbled up their dinner. And the new keeper never forgot who ate what again.

The gnomes of Brooklands Avenue

One summer, a garden fete was held at the biggest house in Brooklands Avenue. On one of the stalls were two plastic garden gnomes for sale.

'Ugh!' sniffed Mrs Fitzchutney. 'They're not the sort of things I like in *my* garden.'

'Indeed not!' snorted Mrs Pringle-Potterton.

Then along came Burt Blogginson, who lived in the smallest cottage in Brooklands Avenue.

'Poor gnomes!' said Burt. 'You'll hurt their feelings. I'll buy them.'

'Blogginson's garden looks such a mess that it doesn't matter what he puts into it,' sniffed Mrs Fitzchutney.

'At least he will have a splash of colour now,' snorted Mrs Pringle-Potterton.

Poor Burt Blogginson's garden was rather a mess. He knew it, but he didn't have the energy to make it look right. The next morning, though, he thought he must be dreaming. The garden was tidy. The lawn was cut, and there were flowers growing in neat rows in the flower beds. It was a riot of colour.

The folk of Brooklands Avenue couldn't believe their eyes.

'How has Burt made his garden so beautiful?' gasped Mrs Fitzchutney.

'How has he done it so quickly?' asked Mrs Pringle-Potterton.

Only Burt Blogginson guessed that his garden gnomes had come to life at night and worked their magic powers on his garden to thank him for giving them a home.

The toys' concert

Susanne was ill in bed and the toys were putting on a show to cheer her up. They were all huddled on the window-sill behind the curtains.

Suddenly, Elephant stuck his head through, his trunk held high. 'Tara, tara tara tara,' he boomed, then disappeared just as quickly.

There were giggles from behind the curtains, then, *sshhh*, everything went quiet. The curtains drew back slowly and there stood Wendy, the beautiful doll, in a sparkling silver dress.

She stood very still while Edward Bear wound up the music box. Wendy danced and twirled very prettily, finishing in a deep curtsey just like a ballerina.

Susanne clapped proudly.

Elephant was next playing the drums. It wasn't very musical but it made Susanne laugh. After Elephant, Jolly and Agatha the rag doll did a funny dance. Agatha's long arms and legs swung in all directions. Then she slipped and fell, burst out laughing and rushed off.

Susanne cheered and cheered. Poor

Jolly looked lost, so the others rushed on quickly and started singing 'Happy Birthday'.

It wasn't anyone's birthday but it was the only song they all knew.

Susanne laughed and joined in too. She was feeling very much better already.

Dippy the duckling

'I'm tired of the duck pond,' said Dippy Duckling, 'I'm going to swim down the river to the sea.'

'The sea will be too rough for a small duckling like you,' said the big drake.

'Pooh, I can take care of myself,' Dippy told the other ducklings, and when they were not looking he started swimming away from the pond.

Suddenly, a water rat poked his head out of the river bank. 'Go away little duckling,' he snarled. 'This is my part of the river,' and he chased Dippy away.

'I'm not afraid,' said Dippy, and he swam on.

Then a big swan came paddling out of the reeds. 'Go away, little duckling,' he hissed. 'This is my part of the river,' and he flapped his wings and chased Dippy away.

'I-I-I'm n-n-not afraid,' said Dippy, and he went swimming on. Then, up the river came a big motor boat. It made a loud, roaring noise and it was going so fast that it made big waves as it rushed past.

'Ooh!' cried Dippy as he rocked about on the waves. 'That must be a big sea monster. I d-don't think I'll go to sea, after all.'

Just then the big drake came swimming up. He took Dippy all the way back to the duck pond, and that was the last anyone ever heard about Dippy Duckling wanting to go to sea.

Jane May

What has happened
To Janey May?
She went away
A month today.

She said she'd return.
But I'm sad to say
There is not a sign
Of Janey May.

Old Gossip Grey
Says Janey may
Or may not return
On Saturday.

So I'll wait at the gate
And there I'll stay
Wishing Jane May
Will come my way.

Poco the bull

Poco was alone in the field. He envied his brave brothers, who had gone with the farmer in his truck to the bullring. Poco dreamed he was there too.

He jumped with fright – a bee buzzed loudly near his ear.

'Ha ha!' laughed the goat as Poco ran to the other end of the field.

Poor Poco blushed with shame and ran off . . . straight into a line of washing.

'Where am I? I can't see,' he cried from under the wet sheet.

'Fancy being scared of that,' laughed the farmer's wife.

Poco blushed again, and ran to hide.

That night, he was awakened by a loud clucking in the hen-house.

'I ought to help those chickens,' he trembled, unable to move. Then he closed his eyes tight, and rushed up to the door. He bellowed loudly.

The door opened, and a brown fox slunk away.

The grateful hens crowded round. 'Thank you, Poco,' they clucked.

The farmer came and saw what Poco had done. He smiled and said to his wife, 'That little bull is brave after all!'

Alexander's trip to the Moon

One day Alexander jumped into his pedal car and said, 'I'm going to the moon.'

'By car?' asked his mummy.

'I've got to get to the rocket launching pad first,' he replied.

'Well cheerio,' said Mummy. 'See you again soon.'

With both hands on the steering wheel Alexander zoomed off – up the garden path, around the clothes-line pole and to a secret place behind the shed.

'Phew!' he breathed. Then he saw Sally who lived next-door coming over to play. 'I'm going to the moon,' he told her.

'Can I come with you?' Sally asked.

'We'll have to pretend we've got a rocket,' explained Alexander, getting out of his car.

But before they had time to pretend about a rocket they both sniffed the air like twitchy-nosed rabbits. A lovely cooking smell of hot cakes was coming from somewhere! As they raced back to Alexander's mummy's kitchen the smell got better and better!

'Hello,' she said. 'You've both come in time to clean out my mixing bowl.'

Together they spooned up the left-over cake mixture from the sides of the bowl. Later they each had a small fruity cake, still warm from the oven.

'We'll go to the moon tomorrow,' agreed Alexander and Sally.

The runaway house

Michael was always threatening to run away and one day the old house heard him. 'Huh! So he'll run away, will he? I'll show him.'

The next day, on his return from school, Michael stood still and gasped. *There* was Number Six The Avenue. *There* was Number Eight The Avenue. But *where* was Number Seven?

'My house has disappeared. It must have heard what I said and so it ran away. Oh, what shall I do?' wailed Michael.

There was only one thing he could do. Michael began searching, and he went on searching for such a long time until, at last, he gave up. 'I'll never find my dear old house again,' he said sadly as he fell asleep.

When he woke, the sun was shining and he heard his mother's voice: 'Michael dear. Breakfast in five minutes. Wake up.'

And then he knew he had been dreaming. His house hadn't run away after all. Then he whispered, 'I'll never threaten to run away again,' and he thought he heard the old house whisper back:

'East, West,
Home's best.'

The dancing coat

One cold winter's day, Jane was on her way to school and met an old woman. 'Young Miss,' said the old woman, 'you're very young. I'm very old. You're very warm. I'm very cold. So give me your coat.'

Jane answered, 'No. I'm sorry you're old. I'm sorry you're cold. But I can't give you my coat.'

'Then dance, coat, dance!' cried the old woman.

The coat began to dance on Jane's shoulders. It whirled round and Jane danced with it – up the street, down the street, all the way to school. She danced into the classroom.

'Stand still!' snapped Miss Grimble, who was a grumbler.

'I c-c-can't,' said poor Jane.

'Take off your coat,' said Miss Grimble. Jane tried but it wouldn't come off. Miss Grimble pulled at it, then she tugged at it and at last it came off. Then – she stared. All the children stared.

For the coat began to dance up to the ceiling, down to the floor, whirled round Miss Grimble then danced out of the door. And only Jane knew that it was dancing away to an old, old, cold, cold woman.

Who likes what?

Peppermint
For Arabella Quint;

Cherry pie
For Isabella Dye;

Cream and honey
For Annabella Bunny;

Chocolate cake
For Catherina Lake;

Apricot crumble
For Wilhelmina Bumble –

BUT toast and tea
For Plain Jane Lea.

162

Simple Simon

Once upon a time, a boy named Simon set off to see the fair. He had to walk a long way, and he began to feel hungry, but along the road he met a Pieman going to the fair.

'May I have one of your pies?' he asked the Pieman.

'You must pay me first,' said the Pieman. 'One penny, if you please.'

'But I haven't got a penny,' said Simon. 'Then you can't have a pie,' said the man.

Simon felt hungrier than ever. But he had an idea. He hurried on to the fair, to find the owner.

'Please sir,' he said, 'I want to earn a penny to buy a pie.'

'Very well,' said the fair owner. 'You can help the Fat Lady to button up her coat.'

So Simon huffed and puffed and

pulled and tugged until at last he had fastened all the buttons on the Fat Lady's coat. She was so pleased that she gave him *five* pennies. And Simon bought *five* pies.

But oh dear – fastening all those buttons and eating all those pies made poor Simon so tired that he fell asleep. And he didn't wake up until the fair was over.

Handsome Oscar

In the street next to ours there used to live a cat named Oscar. He was very proud of his shining black fur, and liked to sit on top of the wall where everyone could see him.

But one day he decided that the wall wasn't high enough. 'Now, if I sit on the roof of the house,' he thought to himself, 'the whole world will be able to see me.'

So he climbed up on to the roof-top, and sat there purring loudly. Soon a crowd of people had gathered below on the pavement and were staring up at him. Some of them were pointing, and calling to each other.

'They're saying what a very handsome cat I am,' thought Oscar proudly.

But then he heard someone shout – 'That poor cat is trapped on the roof. We must rescue him.'

'What!' cried Oscar indignantly. 'Rescue me? Whatever for?'

Before he knew what was happening, a man came with a ladder and carried him carefully down to the pavement. There everyone made a fuss of him, and stroked him, and said what a brave and handsome cat he was.

And Oscar decided that he rather liked being rescued, after all.

The story of Leaf

There was once a little leaf who was born in the springtime high up in a tree in the wood. At first he was only a tiny white bud on one of the branches.

'I wish the sun would shine,' he said.

The spring sun shone, and Leaf slowly uncurled his sides and turned palest green.

As summertime drew nearer, Leaf said, 'I wish the sun would shine even more.'

And as the summer sun shone hotter and hotter, Leaf spread himself right out across his branch in the tree. He lay in the sun all day long, and his colour changed to darkest green.

But when autumn arrived, he noticed that his sides had grown quite wrinkled, and he was beginning to turn brown and thin. Now he said, 'I wish I hadn't stayed out in the sun so long. I am growing withered and old.'

And when the first winds of winter blew, Leaf left the tree and floated away, down and down until he reached the ground. And the snow covered him over.

But when springtime came, another little bud began to grow high up in the tree. And Leaf's story began all over again.

Charlie for short!

Poor Charlotte Elizabeth Alison Jane!
She didn't much care for her rather
long name,
'My friend named Joanna is always
called Jo!
Samantha's called Sam, and I'd like
to know
Why my name is Charlotte?' Oh, how
she'd complain!
That Charlotte Elizabeth Alison Jane!

Then Grandma said; 'Charlotte,
why don't we all
Call you "Charlie" for short? Would
you answer our call,
If we called "Hello, Charlie," then
would you be sad?'
Charlotte said she would smile and be
happy and glad.
She liked "Charlie" better – although
it is plain –
That Charlotte Elizabeth Alison Jane!

Simon's walk

Simon had walked a long way. He came to a horse, looking over a gate. 'Hello Horse,' he said. 'I've run away.'

The horse snorted, and Simon walked on. He climbed a stile, and saw a rabbit.

'Hello Rabbit,' he said. 'I've run away.' But the rabbit flashed the white of his tail and was gone.

Simon walked across the fields, and came to a river. A little boat was on the water and a boy was rowing it. 'Hello Boy,' he said. 'I've run away.'

The boy pulled into the side. 'Would you like a lift in my boat?' Simon's legs hurt a bit, so he clambered in, gratefully.

Dip dip, went the oars, dip dip in the water – and the little boat rocked gently as she went. Simon fell fast asleep.

Fit the biscuits

I've made biscuits
Ready for the tray.

Please will you help
To put them away?

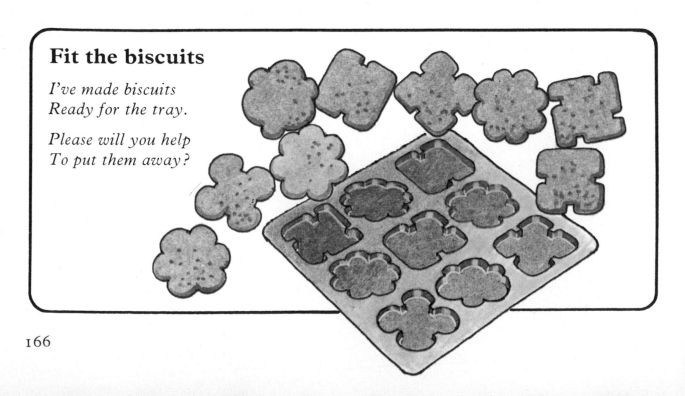

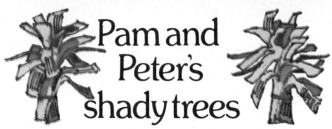

Pam and Peter's shady trees

Later, the boy woke him up. 'I think you'd better get out here,' he said.

Simon thanked him, and climbed up the bank. At the top, he went along a road, then stopped in wonder. He was quite near his home. He'd walked all that way, and the river had brought him back! Suddenly, he felt starving hungry . . . and decided he wouldn't run away after all.

Pam and Peter went to see Grandad. He was digging in the garden. 'Would you like some Lily of the Valley for your garden?' he said. 'It needs a shady spot under some trees.'

'We haven't any shady trees in our garden,' said Peter to Pam.

'Let's make some,' said Pam, when they got home.

So they got some newspapers and tore strips along one side. Then they rolled the other side into a tight stalk and put elastic bands round. And all the torn bits hung down like leaves.

'Just like banana trees!' said Peter as he painted them green and stuck them in the soil.

But it rained and the trees went soggy and floppy.

Then Dad came home carrying a long, thin parcel.

'Been gardening?' he said. 'Yes,' said Pam, 'but our shady paper trees got washed away.'

'Well how about some real ones, then,' said Dad. And he let them open the parcel. 'They're baby apple trees.'

The sun started to shine and Pam and Peter helped Dad to plant the new trees.

'We'll have real shady spots for our Lily of the Valley,' said Pam and Peter happily.

The May Day hat

Mary went to the May Day fair. A man at a stall called: 'Hats! Hats! Buy a fine hat.'

'I'll have that green hat with the red ribbons,' said Mary.

'That one's not for sale,' the man told her. 'Why?' asked Mary.

'*Not for sale*,' he repeated firmly.

Mary put the money on the counter and the hat on her head, and walked away.

'On your own head be it!' he called after her.

Then strange things began to happen to Mary. She saw her friend Jane and called: 'Hello, Jane.' But Jane didn't answer. She walked right past as if Mary was not there.

She saw her Uncle Jonathan.

'Hi, Uncle Jon,' called Mary, but he too passed her by as if he did not see her.

'It's the hat,' thought Mary. 'It has made me invisible,' and she hurried back to the stall.

'A-ha,' said the stallkeeper, 'I knew you'd be back. Having trouble?'

'It's this horrible hat,' Mary replied.

'Give it to me, then,' said the man, but try as she would, Mary could not lift the hat from her head.

The stallkeeper grinned and said some strange words. It was then that she noticed that he had pointed pixie ears and a turned-up mouth.

The hat rose from Mary's head like a cloud and floated to the back of the stall. 'That's odd,' said Mary. '*That's* magic,' said the stallkeeper with a huge grin. 'Never wear a green hat with red ribbons on a May Day.'

And Mary vowed she never would again.

Willie's errands

Willie liked running errands, but only because most people gave him a sweet as a reward. Soon he became careless, and stopped bothering to listen to his instructions properly.

One day Mrs Pinchpenny wanted some mince for dinner. Willie sped off to the shops and soon returned. With one hand he held out the paper bag; the other was open, ready for his toffee. But Mrs Pinchpenny smacked it hard.

'I can't make cottage pie with sweet-shop mints,' she groaned. Next day, Willie found Mr Trimmer tying up his dahlias. 'Please Willie, could you get me six stakes from Mr Mower's?'

Willie ran off and came back with six best beef-steaks from the butcher.

Next day, Willie called on Granny who was sick in bed. He was glad her biscuit tin was by the bed!

'Just run to the kitchen and fetch my slippers, and put them by the bed, Willie,' said Granny. How she jumped when her feet landed on a pair of ice-cold kippers!

Granny pretended to be cross, but Willie never knew how she chuckled when he had gone!

The snake who felt the cold

Sammie Snake was made from red cloth. It was his job to keep the cold draughts away from Jenny and her family.

Every winter evening he lay across the crack under the living-room door and shivered. How pleased he was in summer to curl up in a warm patch of sunlight and sleep.

One morning, before the sun had finally left for its winter holiday, Jenny ran to Mummy.

'The workmen are here,' she cried.

The workmen hammered and bustled about for days. When they left at last and all was tidy again, a gale started to blow.

Sammie shivered, thinking of the crack under the door. Then he realised he wasn't cold. There were no draughts!

'It is nice now that we have central heating in all the rooms,' said Jenny.

'We won't need Sammie Snake again,' said Mummy.

'Can I have him?' asked Jenny.

'We'll give him a bath first,' said Mummy.

So Sammie had a warm bath and was dried in the airing cupboard. Then he lay happily at the foot of Jenny's bed.

The Wilsons' Wednesday walks

Every Wednesday afternoon, Mr Wilson would close the bookshop where he worked, come home, and take his family for a walk.

Mrs Wilson would push their little daughter, Samantha, in her pushchair and their son, Stuart, would skip ahead – stopping to pick up a stick or two.

'I like to have a stick with me,' he would say. 'I can poke it in cracks, or bonk the trunks of trees with it, and zoom it along fences.'

'We'll have to call you "Stuart-Pick-Up-Sticks,"' laughed Mrs Wilson.

When Samantha was old enough not to need her pushchair any longer, she would walk along every Wednesday afternoon with Mr and Mrs Wilson and Stuart.

She noticed Stuart picking up a stick or two, and she began picking things up, too – not a stick or two, but a stone or two!

'I like to have a stone with me,' she would say. 'I can kick it in front of me as I go, or roll it along the ground, and I can plop it into puddles.'

'I think we'll have to call you "Samantha-Pick-Up-Stones,"' laughed Mrs Wilson.

'What a funny sight we must be!' Mr Wilson chuckled. 'Folk must say, "There they go, Mr and Mrs Wilson on their Wednesday walk, with their two funny children – Stuart-Pick-Up-Sticks and Samantha-Pick-Up-Stones."'

The chimpanzees' tea party

Every Saturday in the zoo, the chimpanzees had a tea-party, but it was always spoiled by Busy Bluebottle. He was a real nuisance, buzzing round everyone, spoiling their games and eating their food.

One day the chimps made a plan to teach Busy Bluebottle a lesson. They set out the tea-party, and in the middle of the table they put a large jar of strawberry jam.

Busy Bluebottle couldn't resist strawberry jam.

'Whoopee,' he shouted, 'BZZZ,' and dived straight in, head first!

Oh, what a sticky mess! The jam stuck to his wings and his legs, and try as he might, he couldn't get out.

'BZZZ, help,' he shouted. 'Help.'

The chimpanzees looked at him through the glass jar.

'Will you promise to leave us alone?' they asked.

'Oh, yes,' cried Busy Bluebottle. 'But please get me out.'

So the chimps took him out of the jar and dropped him into a bowl of cold water to wash off the jam.

'Brrr,' shivered Bluebottle as he flew off. 'I don't think tea-parties are much fun after all.'

Rivals

I was four and soon after my birthday
I decided I'd marry Clare,
But she said she was marrying Ronnie,
My friend from Cadogan Square.

I gave her my very best conker ;
Crafty Ron let her have his white mouse.
I said she could borrow my lizard ;
Ronnie offered to paint her doll's house.

I then let her play with my puppy
But Ron's kitten soon won her back ;
I felt sure she was mine when I gave her
A fine rubber duck that could quack.

But we found that she couldn't be trusted,
For she said she was marrying Tony.
We agreed we could not really blame her –
She had been for a ride on his pony.

Princess Petulenta

Even princesses have to be taught, but Princess Petulenta refused to learn anything. She ate with her fingers, ran barefoot in the rain, and demanded breakfast at tea-time.

'I've had enough!' sighed the queen when Petulenta was eighteen.

'She must marry,' declared the king.

But Petulenta liked none of the princes she met. She was bored as a princess, so she put on a cap and apron and washed dishes in the royal kitchen.

A new baker was appointed. As Petulenta watched him knead the spongy dough her heart ached to make crispy loaves and sugary doughnuts.

'Teach me,' she pleaded, but he never answered.

'Poor man. He is deaf and dumb,' she thought, and tried to be polite and helpful, even tidy.

One day he made her a tiny loaf.

Inside was a message:
Make no mistake,
Marry me
And learn to bake.

'Marry a baker!' stormed the king.

'Impossible!' wailed the queen.

But Petulenta said, 'He is the first person who never tried to teach me anything. I will marry him!'

At the wedding the baker's voice returned. He told everyone he had only pretended to be dumb so as to win Petulenta! She became the best cook in the land, and forgot she had been bored.

Mandy's magic bonnet

Mandy stared. Mummy was buried under a pile of hats.

'These are for the Jumble Sale,' she said.

Then Mandy saw *the special one*. It was a black straw one with long ribbons to tie under the chin.

'Where did that come from?' wondered Mummy, pushing it aside. 'No one will buy that old thing.'

'Can I have it, Mummy?' asked Mandy. In her bedroom she tried it on and then something strange happened. She began to float! She floated right out of the window, high above the streets, until she came to Buckingham Palace. She landed just as they were changing the guard. The people watching wore old-fashioned clothes, and the ladies had hats like hers.

A soldier in his bright red uniform saluted her. 'Come with me,' he said.

Surprised, Mandy followed him into the palace. He knocked on a door and Mandy went in.

Counting eggs

My white hen lays two eggs,
My brown hen lays three.
Lucy has one for breakfast,
Jamie has one for tea.
How many eggs does that leave for me?

'Have some tea,' smiled a little old lady as she handed Mandy a cup. Mandy knew who she was. She had seen pictures of her in a book.

Then, in a wink of the eye, Mandy was in her own bedroom taking off the bonnet.

Mummy called, 'Tea's ready.'

Mandy smiled. Mummy would not believe that she had been to tea with Queen Victoria at Buckingham Palace, but we do, don't we?

Inch Elf, Lucy and Oliver Otter

Inch Elf and Lucy Ladybird woke up early. They were feeling happy.

Inch Elf was taking Lucy Ladybird to the river bank to meet his friend Oliver Otter. Oliver was busy as usual, repairing the river bank when Inch and Lucy arrived.

'Good morning Oliver,' called Inch. 'I would like you to meet Lucy Ladybird. She has come to stay in my house.'

'I'm going to swim down the river this morning,' Oliver told Inch and Lucy. 'Why don't you come with me?'

'That would be fun,' said Inch. 'We would love to come.' And they both hopped on to a waterlily.

The waterlily floated down the river, and Oliver Otter swam behind, pushing it along with his nose.

It was late when they returned to the river bank, and Inch and Lucy thanked Oliver for a lovely day, then went home to Buttercup Wood for a long sleep.

Sporting Riddles

Come riddle me west and riddle me east
And I wish you plenty of luck.
What bird do cricketers like least?
The answer, of course, is a duck.

Come riddle by night and riddle by day
And riddle all over the place.
What card do tennis-players like to play?
There's only one answer – an ace.

Come riddle me heat and riddle me frost
And riddle me this, if you dare.
Why do some boxers look so lost?
Because they fight in a ring that's square.

Come riddle me now and riddle me then,
But riddle me this time right.
Why are anglers all like hungry men?
Because they're waiting for a bite.

The magic chair

One day Mark, who was five years old, went with his Mother to a very old furniture shop. They bought a chair for Mark's bedroom.

Mark didn't like the chair much. He thought his friend Michael's rocking chair was nicer.

'It will last longer than Michael's rocking chair,' Mark's Mother told him gently. 'That chair is over two hundred years old.'

'Two hundred years,' whispered Mark, 'I wonder who has sat on you — maybe a King.' Mark decided he liked the chair after all, and sat down on it.

He had just opened his picture book, when a strange thing happened. The people in the pictures started to move. Mark stared in amazement.

On the page was an old King. The King stepped out of the book. 'So you're the new owner of my throne,' he said. 'Y-y-es, Y-y-your Majesty,' stammered Mark.

'Take care of it,' ordered the King.

'I will,' agreed Mark.

'Am I dreaming?' Mark said aloud.

'No,' said the chair. 'Don't tell anyone what you have seen. Only if the secret is kept will you see my magic powers.'

'And I thought a rocking chair was fun,' Mark chuckled.

The singing barber of Salisbury Town

Way down in Salisbury Town there lived a barber. All day long he sang as he cut his customers' hair. He sang popular songs and old-fashioned songs. He sang bass, tenor and alto. He even did a little tap dance as he circled around each customer.

'Clip, clip,' went his scissors.

'Oh, for the wings of a dove,' sang the barber.

'Tippety, tap,' went his feet.

And his customers? They loved it! They clapped their hands to his singing. They beat out the rhythm with their feet. And sometimes if they knew the words they even joined in the chorus.

There was only one thing wrong with the singing barber of Salisbury Town – he only sang one song to each customer.

If the song was short, the barber hadn't enough time. Sometimes the customer's hair was hardly cut at all!

If the song was long, the barber kept cutting and cutting. Sometimes the customer was clipped almost bald!

But with all that merriment, I never even heard anyone complain.

The rose tree

A poor widow had nothing in the world except a tumbledown cottage, a patch of ground and one barren rose tree.

One day a small child came to the door and asked, 'Could you spare me a crust of bread? I am so very hungry.'

The widow answered, 'I have nothing much to give, my poor child, but you're welcome to share what I have.' She went into the kitchen for food and, while doing so, she saw through the window that the girl was touching the barren rose tree. She called to her, 'Be careful, my child. That tree has no roses but it has some very spiteful thorns.'

The girl turned and smiled at her and the widow saw to her amazement that she was no longer a poor thin child, but a bright and shining creature. She ran into the garden wondering who the strange child could be, but she had disappeared. Where the child had touched the tree, however, the loveliest roses bloomed in crimson, white, yellow and pink.

It was a miracle indeed, for, when winter came and there was not a flower to be seen in all the land, the widow's rose tree still blossomed. People came from far and near, through frost and snow, to buy the precious roses.

And the widow never went cold or hungry again.

'Can't play with me,' the toy soldier shouted as Patrick bent down to him.

'Don't touch,' the rag doll held up her hands as Angela reached out to her.

The battery-driven tank sped under the bed. The stuffed bear jumped behind the curtains. All the other toys – the rocking-horse, the paper dragon, the elephant with the wobbly ears – jumped into the toy box.

The marionette clown slammed the lid and sat on it. 'Hands off!' he cried. 'We're on strike!'

'On strike for what?' Patrick and Angela asked in amazement.

'We're not cared for,' the clown answered. 'My strings are broken. The soldier needs painting. All the others are battered and broken. If you sign this paper, we'll let you play with us.' He held up a sheet.

'*We promise to repair our toys*,' Patrick read slowly. He signed his name. Then Angela signed hers.

'Right,' the clown said. 'The strike's over.' He jumped off the box and all the toys came out.

But there wasn't any playing with them for almost a week. It took that long for Patrick and Angela painting, patching and mending to keep their part of the agreement.

No wonder the toys struck!

The patchwork cushion

Janet was six years old and she lived with her parents and two brothers.

One day her mother said, 'It's Granny's birthday in a week's time – what shall we give her?'

Daddy suggested a big bunch of flowers but Janet said, 'I would like to make her a new cushion cover. She has a hole in her old one.'

So Mummy showed her how to make a patchwork cushion. She found lots of pretty pieces of cotton material and showed Janet how to cut brown-paper squares and sew them on the pieces of material. Janet worked hard until she had enough squares for one side of the cushion and then her mother taught her how to sew each square together with tiny stitches.

'Now we have the back to do,' said Mummy, but this time she helped Janet by using the sewing machine to sew one large piece of material to the back of the squares.

Afterwards, Janet watched Mummy sew on hooks and eyes to stop the cushion falling out.

On her birthday Granny was pleased with the flowers, but best of all she loved the cushion cover. 'I think it's the nicest present I've ever had,' she said.

The tail of the Siamese cat

Long ago there was a beautiful princess who always wore lovely dresses and lots of rings on her fingers. Everywhere the princess went she was followed by her Siamese cat.

One day the princess was walking by the river. 'How cool the water looks,' said the princess. 'I would love to bathe in the river today.'

There was no one else in sight, so the princess began to take off her lovely dress. 'Where can I put my rings so I don't lose them?' she wondered.

The Siamese cat gave a loud cry and stood with his tail stretched out. 'Oh, I can put my rings on your tail,' said the princess. 'What a clever cat you are!'

The Siamese cat stood very still, so that the rings would not fall off.

The princess enjoyed swimming in the cool river so much that she didn't come out for ages. When she did come back to the bank, the Siamese cat's tail had bent in the middle, because the rings were so heavy.

And do you know, ever since then, every true Siamese cat has been born with a kink in its tail.

How many monkeys?

Two little monkeys
Lived inside the zoo.
Then they had some children –
First three,
Then one,
Then two.

How many monkeys
Now live inside the zoo?

The adventures of the Chimney-Pot Mice

In Cribbins wood stands an old cottage. At the bottom of the chimney, in a snug little nest, live the Chimney-Pot Mice.

One morning, the Chimney-Pot Mice scampered through the wood. As they passed an oak tree, a surprising thing happened. A bright red door in the tree trunk opened, and out peered a little dwarf.

'Hello,' called the mice, 'Who are

you?' 'I'm Fen,' replied the dwarf. 'Would you like to come in?'

The mice were delighted. They entered a cosy room and sat upon wooden chairs. Fen was very excited. 'Look what I have found,' he said, and spread on the table a piece of yellow parchment.

'What is it?'

'A treasure map.'

'Treasure!' squeaked the Chimney-Pot Mice, 'May we help you find it?'

'Yes,' said Fen. 'Let's meet outside my front door at midnight.'

The moon watched as Fen and the three little mice dug a deep hole. Eventually, they found a wooden casket. Inside sparkled four silver pennies.

'How lovely!' squeaked the Chimney-Pot Mice.

'A coin for each of us,' smiled Fen. 'I treasure my new friends more than silver pennies – come for tea tomorrow.'

'We will,' called the mice. 'Goodnight, Fen.'

'Goodnight, Chimney-Pot Mice.'

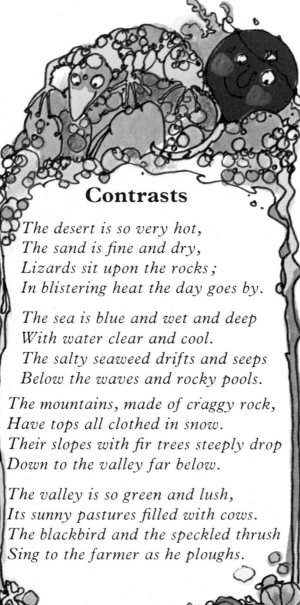

Contrasts

The desert is so very hot,
The sand is fine and dry,
Lizards sit upon the rocks;
In blistering heat the day goes by.

The sea is blue and wet and deep
With water clear and cool.
The salty seaweed drifts and seeps
Below the waves and rocky pools.

The mountains, made of craggy rock,
Have tops all clothed in snow.
Their slopes with fir trees steeply drop
Down to the valley far below.

The valley is so green and lush,
Its sunny pastures filled with cows.
The blackbird and the speckled thrush
Sing to the farmer as he ploughs.

Seeds bring surprises

A thick hedge grew round a cottage garden. Blackbirds built nests in it, sparrows gossiped there, and chaffinches played hide-and-seek amongst the leaves.

But then a new owner came. He cut down the hedge and built a high brick wall, and the birds stopped singing and flew away. 'I've no use for flowers,' said Mr Tidy, and he pulled up the lavender, sweet-williams and hollyhocks, and planted cabbages.

Some cheeky stinging-nettles peeped over the wall.

'Weeds bring seeds,' grumbled Mr Tidy.

'And seeds bring surprises!' rumbled the wind as he blew across the neighbouring field.

Faster than Mr Tidy could hoe, the wind blew seeds over the wall. 'Oh, let them grow,' he said, giving up. 'I'll move back to town, away from the weeds.'

But two weeks later he heard a thrush singing: 'Birds need trees, flowers need bees. Give us these.'

Mr Tidy went outside. He rubbed his eyes. Flowers grew everywhere, bees buzzed contently, and a butterfly settled on his sleeve. A robin sang, 'Don't leave us,' and all the birds joined in.

And so Mr Tidy stayed. He planted trees and bought a beehive, and he didn't worry any more about the weeds.

Find the rabbits

Six little rabbits
In the morning dew,
Ate the farmer's lettuces
And all his carrots too.

Six little rabbits
Didn't stop to play;
When the farmer came along
They soon ran away.

Six little rabbits
Jumped in the air –
Look carefully in the garden,
They're hiding everywhere.

Aunty May's twins

'Here's Aunty May with her new twins,' said Pam to Peter. 'The pram's got a baby at each end, and they both look the same.'

'They were born on the same day,' said Aunty May. 'Dorothy came first, then John.'

Then Aunty May went to talk to Pam and Peter's Mum.

Peter and Pam smiled at the twins. But, oh my – one of them started to cry: 'Woo – woowow, wairair.'

It gave Peter such a shock that he ran to tell Aunty May.

'One of the babies is crying,' he said.

'Little babies often cry,' said Aunty. 'Which one is it?'

'The one in the white bonnet,' said Peter.

'They've *both* got white bonnets,' said Pam.

'Even I get muddled up when they're asleep with their clothes on and their eyes shut,' said Aunty May.

So Pam and Peter helped Aunty May. They fetched two pieces of paper and their coloured pencils and crayoned a D for Dorothy and put it at Dorothy's end of the pram. Then they put a J for John at John's end.

'Now we shall never get muddled up again,' laughed Aunty May. 'Thank you, Pam and Peter.'

The king who wanted to be a giant

Once upon a time there was a king who wanted to be a giant. So his magician chanted a spell:

'*Ho, ho,*
The king's too low.
Taller, taller
He must grow.'

The king grew and grew, until he touched the ceiling.

'I'm *gigantic*!' he said.

He sat on his throne, but it broke under his weight, and he fell with a bump on the floor. He stood up, and banged his head on the ceiling.

'I'll go outside,' he said, 'and show my subjects how gigantic I am.'

The door was too low, so he lay on the floor and started to crawl through, but his head got stuck. He lay there for two hours, while the magician tried to remember the spell to make him small.

At last, the magician exclaimed, 'I've got it!'

'*Jig, jig,*
The king's too big.
Wink, blink,
The king must shrink.'

The king shrank like a balloon, until he was his ordinary size again.

'I don't want to be a giant after all,' he said, 'but I've got a *gigantic* appetite – bring me my dinner!'

Puppy

I'd love a puppy
Loose and floppy,
Warm and soft,
Gambolly, loppy.

Jumping, tumbling,
Rolling we'd be,
Tugging and hugging
My puppy and me.

Joe, the blue car

You see, Joe didn't live in a garage and in the wet weather the rain got under his bonnet and dripped onto his engine.

Mrs Smith said to her husband 'Poor Joe, he's not very happy standing out in the open. Why don't we build a garage for him?'

So they did. And now Joe lives in a brand new brick garage all of his own. In the mornings, he starts up first time and Mr Smith is very pleased and says, 'Well done, Joe.'

And Joe replies, 'Honk, honk,' as off to work they go.

Joe was a little blue car. He had two doors, a very shiny bonnet and a row of badges on his front bumper. He belonged to Mr and Mrs Smith and he lived in the country.

Joe drove Mr Smith to work in the mornings but sometimes he couldn't start his engine and Mr Smith would get cross with him. 'Hurry up, Joe, or I'll be late,' he would say.

'I'm trying hard,' said Joe, 'but I do feel so cold and damp.'

The frog who talked too much

Once there was a frog named Frogo who was a great chatterbox. His father, mother and sister were always begging him to stop talking. But Frogo chattered and chattered.

One day, as Frogo the Frog hopped over a log, he fell and cut his big mouth. It hurt. He hurried to the Animal Hospital.

'O-Ho!' said Dr Rat. 'That's a nasty cut. That will need stitching.' And he stitched up Frogo's mouth and sent him home.

'What have you done to your mouth, son?' asked his father.

Frogo couldn't answer.

'My poor baby. What is it?' cried his mother.

Frogo could not answer.

His sister Floss laughed, 'Hahaha, he went for a walk. When he came back, he just couldn't talk. *Hooray!*'

And Frogo couldn't answer back. Even worse, he couldn't eat his favourite dinner – water-lily icecream.

For seven days he could neither speak nor eat, and he didn't know which was worse. When he went back to the hospital Dr Rat said, 'A-HA! Time those stitches came out.' He snip-snipped with his scissors and at last Frogo could open his mouth again.

And what do you think his first words were? 'I'm hungry. Let's eat.'

Where's Jolly?

Peter gazed around Jolly's field. No Jolly!

He was alarmed and ran to find Mr Barnaby. 'Are you using Jolly today?' he panted.

'No,' said Jolly's owner. 'Is anything wrong?'

Peter told him, and Mr Barnaby was worried. 'Let me look for him!' Peter said, running off.

A man had fallen off his bike, and was picking his scattered onions up. 'Have you seen a horse?' gasped Peter. The man was cross, and pointed: 'More like an elephant!'

'That's Jolly!' said Peter eagerly.

'JOLLY?' barked the man. 'You call him Jolly? Look at my onions!'

But Peter had gone. On he ran, then he heard shouting and a man rushed out of a farmyard. 'Mind out boy! We need the army in there to catch that horse.'

'Let me,' said Peter.

The man roared with laughter, as

The missing chicks

*Here comes the farmer with sacks of
    grain
It's time to feed his brood again.
The cock crows, 'Cock-a-doodle-doo!'
The doves call, 'Curroo! Curroo!'
'Quack! quack!' squawk the ducks
But the white hen sadly clucks,
'Where, oh where are my little chicks?
They're always hiding and playing
    tricks.'
Can you show poor Mrs Hen
Where her chicks are hiding, then?*

Peter ran in. There, was poor Jolly, rearing up, cornered by half a dozen men.

'You're frightening him,' shouted Peter, who was upset. To their amazement, he pushed past them, and calmed the trembling horse.

'Well!' exclaimed one. 'To think how it frightened us!' He helped Peter put a halter on Jolly, and take him home. Mr Barnaby was very glad to see Jolly safe. But still no-one knows how Jolly got out of his field. Perhaps some careless person left the gate open!

The vain Princess

Somewhere, through cloud and dreams, stood a castle. Inside, lived a beautiful Princess. But all she could think about, was herself. 'How beautiful I am, I am!' she cried everywhere, and ordered a hundred different mirrors to reflect her in a hundred different ways.

Then, two Princes fell in love with her. The Queen said hopefully, 'She will marry one and forget her vanity.'

But the Princess ignored both, and still had only eyes for herself.

In despair, the King sent for the court magician. 'You must make my daughter ugly,' he told him. So, that night, the Magician cast his spell.

Morning dawned, and the Princess went to a mirror. The mirror cracked! She rushed round the hundred different mirrors, and they cracked in a hundred different ways.

'How ugly I am, I am!' she cried everywhere, and sobbed.

One prince turned away in horror. 'Goodbye,' he said.

The other, dried her tears. 'I don't care what you look like,' he said, 'it's the inside that matters.'

From that day, she was very much in love and never thought about herself. And when the King knew she had changed for good, he ordered the Magician to remove the spell.

Lucy Bodkin's pleasant surprise

One day Lorna the goat, who belonged to Lucy Bodkin, went for a walk and found an acorn. It was a real beauty and Lorna decided to play with it. She balanced it on the end of her nose and tossed it high in the air. Then off she went, balancing and tossing and dancing playfully all the way home.

'That's a fine acorn,' said Lucy Bodkin. 'But pigs like acorns and you are a goat. Let's give it to a pig.'

But instead of keeping it safely until a hungry pig came along, Lorna balanced and tossed it once more – and then she lost it.

Well, Lorna forgot all about that acorn and so did Lucy Bodkin. They forgot about it for many weeks and months and by that time something very interesting had happened . . . a tiny green oak tree had begun to grow in the corner of the garden!

'Now that is a pleasant surprise,' said Lucy.

'Ma-a-a,' said Lorna, suddenly remembering the acorn. 'I planted it.'

Together the funny little lady and her goat looked happily at the tiny tree.

'You clever little goat,' said Lucy. 'One day it will be a great big acorn tree and we'll invite pigs from all around to a party.'

An acorn takes a very long time to grow into an oak though!

Guess what I am.

My first is in sun and also in shine,
My second in yours but not in mine;
My third is in stop but not in go,
My fourth is in ebb but not in flow;
My whole is something which
always lies
Above your mouth and between
your eyes.

The door that wouldn't close

Jane Lane's brother Phil always left doors open.

'Shut the door, Phil,' called his father.

'Shut the door, Phil,' begged his mother.

'Shut the door,' said Jane.

'DOOR,' shouted his brother Tom.

But Phil still left doors open. One evening, as Phil did his school homework, Tom put on a new record which sounded all over the house. No one could study in such a din and, for once, Phil *closed* his bedroom door. It flew open. He closed it again. It flew open again.

'Father,' called Phil, 'could you come and shut my door?'

Mr Lane came to Phil's room and closed the door. It flew open. 'That's odd,' said Mr Lane. Then he called to his wife to come. She shut the door. It flew open. She called to Jane. Jane came and banged it shut. It flew open. Jane called to Tom but the noise of his latest pop record was so loud that he couldn't hear.

Mr Lane, his face very red, went to Tom's room, lifted the record from the machine and said, '*No more.*'

At last there was silence and then – Phil's door closed gently . . . all by itself.

Wendy's pretend friend

It was raining. Wendy wished she had a real friend to play with, but she only had her dollies.

'Cheer up,' said Mummy, 'I saved this for a rainy afternoon.'

Wendy stared. It was a book, shaped like a little girl with fair hair.

'This is a cut-out dolly. Her name's Sue,' said Mummy, cutting round the edge with scissors. Then she opened the book. There were Sue's pretty clothes. A red dress, blue coat, blue straw hat, and a pair of shoes.

When the dolly was dressed, Wendy pretended she was a real little girl.

'This is my new friend, Sue,' she told her dollies. What a lovely time they had!

After tea, Mummy said, 'Bedtime, Wendy.'

The paper dolly watched. Betsy was tucked in her cradle and Jean and Gina side by side in the pram, with Teddy at the foot.

'And you can sleep here,' said Wendy putting the little cut-out figure on the pillow beside her.

'I'm glad you are my friend,' Wendy smiled.

Emily and Pasha

Emily lived in the country, and one of the things she loved best of all was to go for long walks. Emily was very lucky because she had a dog called Pasha who also enjoyed a nice long walk.

Today Emily had decided that she would collect a leaf from all the different trees that they passed during their walk. She picked up her little wicker basket and put it over her arm.

They set off and were soon on their way dancing through the grass and the flowers. There were lots of wild flowers in the meadow. Emily did not know all their names but she loved them all just the same. Soon they were in the forest. They passed lots of trees on the way and Emily carefully picked a leaf from each of them to put in her basket. There were big trees and little trees and in-between trees. Emily even found a tiny oak tree which had grown from an acorn dropped by a bird.

While Emily was busy collecting leaves, Pasha was busy collecting sticks.

When they got home Emily gave Pasha a biscuit and made herself a cup of hot chocolate. Then she sorted out all her leaves on the kitchen table, and laid them inside a scrapbook, holding them in place with a long piece of sellotape.

Later that day Emily would take her paint-box and pencils, copy out each leaf very carefully on some paper and write its name underneath. If there were any that she did not know she would look them up in the library the next time she went to the village. That way she would remember them always.

190

The magic pot

Mrs Jollytop asked her new neighbour, Mrs Lazyboots, to lunch. There was only an empty pot on the table, but Mrs Jollytop said, 'Pot, kindly give me Irish stew,' and soon the pot was brimming with a delicious stew.

Greedy Mrs Lazyboots had three helpings, and the pot was still full. 'It must be magic,' she thought. Then, Mrs Jollytop murmured something to the pot, and it was empty once again.

Next day, when Mrs Jollytop was out, naughty Mrs Lazyboots borrowed the pot. 'Pot, kindly give me runny strawberry jam,' she said.

The pot was soon full of bubbling jam. Mrs Lazyboots happily filled all the glass jars she had ready. But, oh dear, she couldn't remember what stopped the pot boiling. And the runny jam flowed out of the pot over the cooker, down onto the floor, across the passage and under the front door. 'Stop!' squealed Mrs Lazyboots.

When Mrs Jollytop came home, she saw the trail of jam oozing down Mrs Lazyboots' path. She guessed what had happened. She shouted, 'Thank you, Pot. That will do,' and the pot stopped making jam.

But it took days for Mrs Lazyboots to clear up her house. She will never again borrow anything without asking.

Pick a flower

My home is in the meadow grass.
I feel your footsteps as you pass,
But I am hidden from your eye
When I am young and very shy.
In time the sun bids me be bold
And lift my head to shine like gold.
Sometimes my gold is stored away
In bottles for a special day,
Then all the brightness that is mine
Is tasted in the sparkling wine.
When I grow old my head grows white,
Gone is my youth so bold and bright.
But should you need the time to know,
My clock is waiting — blow, blow, blow.

What am I?

Food fit for a King

King Rupert was tired of rich, fancy food. 'I'd like some sausages,' he sighed.

'Kings don't eat *sausages*!' cried the shocked Royal Cook.

One day, the King took off his velvet robe and his crown, and walked into the city, and the most delicious smell of cooking tickled his royal nose.

There was a café, and a sign over the glass front read: *BLOGGS – FOOD FIT FOR KINGS.*

King Rupert went inside. 'What food is fit for a king?' he asked.

'Sausages and chips, sir!' beamed Mr Bloggs the café owner.

'What a sensible man!' thought the King.

Mr Bloggs handed the King a plate of hot, sizzling sausages and golden crispy chips. Very soon, the plate was empty.

'Delicious!' beamed His Majesty. 'A page shall call every day from my palace to fetch a plateful of your sausages and chips.'

'From the p-palace!' stammered Mr Bloggs, for he had not recognised the King without his robes and crown.

'I am King Rupert!' said His Majesty.

'Well!' gasped the astonished Mr Bloggs. And now, the King enjoys his daily sausages and the sign above Mr Bloggs' shop reads: *SAUSAGE FRIER TO HIS MAJESTY THE KING!*

Henry the sad hyena

Henry was supposed to be a laughing hyena but he couldn't find anything funny to make him laugh. All the other hyenas would titter at the silliest thing anybody said, but Henry couldn't even smile.

'I will dance for you,' said Olive the Ostrich, his best friend. Her dance was very peculiar, but Henry didn't think it was funny.

Then Olive asked the best monkey acrobats to perform for Henry; but he just thanked them politely. Next she asked the parrots to tell some funny stories; but Henry couldn't see the jokes. 'I'll just have to go on being the saddest hyena in the world,' he sighed.

'Sometimes it's nice to be different,' said Olive. But she knew that Henry really wanted to be like the others. She began to scratch herself thoughtfully.

'Why are you doing that?' asked Henry.

'I feel itchy,' said Olive. 'I think I'm going to moult.' She fluffed her feathers and some of them fell out. One floated right under Henry's nose. 'That's a funny feeling,' he said, and began to giggle.

'Why, you're *ticklish*!' cried Olive. She took another feather and tickled Henry behind the ears. Once he started laughing, he couldn't stop. By the time Olive had finished moulting Henry was the happiest hyena in all the world.

The helpful cloud

There was once a cloud, frothy as whipped egg-white. He floated on high, imagining that everyone was pleased to see him.

But on the beach the sunbathers felt his shadow and shivered. 'Don't spoil our holiday,' they grumbled.

Like a blotchy ink-stain he dropped towards a man polishing his car. The man shook his fist.

'All right, I'll go where I'm wanted,' huffed the cloud, mischievously spilling some raindrops.

Far away, he found some parched fields. A farmer looked sadly at his wilting corn. Imagine his joy when a heavy shower tumbled down!

When he peeped into little Tom's bedroom the sun was setting. Tom could not get to sleep. Immediately, the cloud became a long pink coral reef, and Tom saw a wonderful picture in the sky of purple islands in a sea of gold. He fell asleep, while the cloud drifted contentedly away.

Big Hat

His name was Anthony Arthur Burlington-Smythe. But everyone called him Big Hat. It was 'Big Hat, come here.' And 'Big Hat, do that.' And 'Big Hat, to bed.' But it was always Big Hat. Never Anthony Arthur Burlington-Smythe.

And why was he called Big Hat, you ask? That's easy – because he wore big hats.

In the winter he wore a wool cap. It covered his head. It came down to his shoulders and half over his chest. And it kept him very, very warm in winter, he said.

In summer he wore a great cowboy hat. Its brim was wider than he was tall. He had to bend sideways to get through the front door. But it kept the hot sun off. At least that's what he said.

And when it rained? Then he wore a sou'wester . . . a great rubbery oilskin thing. It hung down to his feet. The rain poured all around. But not a drop ever touched him he said.

'Yes, big hats are useful,' Big Hat admitted. 'I shall enjoy them while I can. Because when I grow up all this is over. Then it's funny *little* hats, useless *little* hats . . . like father's!'

Legs

If Betty sat
On a three-legged stool
And Billy sat on a chair,
Counting Betty and Billy's
Legs too –
How many legs are there?

Snooky's wedding

'I'll just go to the shops and get my comic,' said Kevin. 'I'll go on my trike, but you can come too, Snooky.'

Snooky wagged his little white tail. He liked going to the shops with Kevin.

'Be a good dog, and guard my trike,' said Kevin when they were in the car park.

But when Kevin came out of the shop he stopped to watch some wedding cars going to the church next to the shops, and he ran home to tell Mum – because she liked weddings. 'But where's your trike?' asked Mum.

'And where's Snooky?' said Dad.

Kevin ran back to get them – but the car park was full of cars. No trike and no Snooky . . .

'What's up sonny?' said an ice-cream man in his van.

'My tricycle's gone,' said Kevin.

'I put it over on the grass by the church,' explained the man. 'It's safer there.'

But when Kevin looked he saw something else . . .

The bride and bridegroom were having their photos taken – with a little white dog.

When they got home, Snooky shook himself and the confetti and silver bells and tiny lucky horseshoes fell out of his fur. And he wagged his tail.

The lady who liked swimming

The lady next door certainly liked swimming. When Sarah rose in the morning she heard her splashing in her pool. When Sarah came home from school she heard her diving. And when Sarah went to bed she heard her swimming.

Sarah couldn't see in next door. The hedge was too thick. No one else had seen the lady either. The milkman saw her left hand once as she reached for the bottle on her doorstep. The breadman saw her right hand when she picked up her loaf. But that was all.

One day Sarah thought and thought. Then she tossed a ball over the hedge. It landed in the pool. 'May I have my ball?' Sarah called.

'Yes,' came the answer.

Sarah pushed through the hedge. A lady with long hair was in the pool, her head just above the water. She held out the ball.

'Thank you,' Sarah said taking it. As she left she said to herself, 'just a lady with long hair. How disappointing.'

As Sarah crawled through the hedge the lady started swimming again.

Look back, Sarah, quickly! Did you ever see a lady with a giant, green fishtail before?

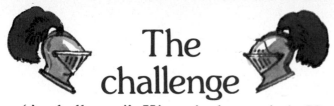

The challenge

'A challenge!' King Arthur cried. He looked again at the letter from Mordred the Morbid. 'He's issued a challenge. But no one can defeat my Knights of the Round Table. Trumpeter, sound your horn.'

The great blast brought Arthur's knights running.

'We've been challenged,' the King repeated, waving his crown in one hand, the letter in the other. 'To horse. Follow me.'

Under cloudy skies Arthur and his knights galloped out of Camelot. For hours they rode through thick forests.

Finally they came to an open field. The army of Mordred the Morbid was drawn up on the other side.

Arthur chose ten of his best men, Mordred ten of his. Then the two leaders advanced towards each other. Arthur reached for his sword. Mordred for his battleaxe. Quick as lightning, Arthur drew first.

'I won. I choose to defend,' he cried. He placed his crown on the ground and stood before it, sword at the ready.

Mordred sent his men into the field and prepared to bowl.

And so the cricket match continued until rain stopped play. For no knights, no matter how valiant, can run, bat or bowl in armour stiffened with rust!

Pixie Town

*We don't need umbrellas
When rain's tumbling down,
We pixies are living
In Tall-Toadstool-Town.
And if you would visit,
There's a ten-thirty train
Which stops at Tall-Toadstool-Town
Now and again.*

197

The toys' picnic

'Here's a good spot,' announced Edward Bear, so while Agatha laid the cloth out on the grass the toys unpacked the picnic basket.

Wendy had made a lovely apple pie, Lion had cut some rather fat sandwiches and there was lemonade.

Elephant handed out plastic forks and spoons and Pussycat gave everyone a paper cup and plate.

They were having such fun that no-one noticed it had started to rain.

Suddenly, there was a loud clap of thunder and the rain poured down.

'Quick, under the bridge,' cried Edward. They all dashed off, grabbing a sandwich as they went and left poor Edward in the rain.

He packed the food quickly back in the basket, putting the odd biscuit in his mouth to save time. Then, he threw the table cloth over his head and ran for cover.

Poor Edward – he was soaked but everyone helped rub him down with paper napkins. They played I Spy and sang nursery rhymes until the rain stopped. It wasn't quite what they had planned, but they all enjoyed it just the same.

How many can you count?

One apple hung upon a tree,
Two eggs lay on a plate,
Three ships went sailing on the sea,
Four birds sat on a gate.

Five marbles rolled along the ground
Six seeds began to grow,
And seven soldiers marched around
A fort, all in a row.

Eight icecreams melted in the sun,
Nine clouds brought lots of rain,
Ten trumpets blew; now just for fun
Count all of them again.

The greedy kitten

Twinkle was a very greedy little kitten. She would eat anything that was lying around.

One day her mistress put a very, very large bowl of cream in the cupboard, and forgot to shut the door. Twinkle crept in and lapped up the cream to the very last drop.

She turned to walk back to her basket, but her tummy was so full that she was round like a ball and she rolled right across the floor. She rolled back and bumped against the table leg.

'Ouch,' she cried, but when she tried to get up she just rolled over!

'Oh dear, what shall I do,' she cried, but there was nothing she could do. She was so fat she couldn't move.

It was a long time before her tummy went down enough for her to waddle slowly back to her basket. She felt very miserable, so she lay down and fell asleep. She woke up with such a tummy-ache that she didn't want any dinner.

Poor Twinkle, she had learnt her lesson the hard way, but after that she was very much better-behaved.

Matchbox fun

William was in bed. He had a bad cold, so he wasn't allowed to go to school. He didn't mind, though, because his Mum always thought of nice things for him to do.

'I've got an idea,' said William's Mum, sitting down on the edge of his bed after lunch. 'We have to fit thirty objects in a matchbox by the time Dad comes home from work.'

'*Aaatishoo*! Thirty!' exclaimed William with a sneeze. 'We'll never do it.'

'I bet we will,' replied Mum. 'Here's a pencil and paper. Let's make a list of the things we think will be small enough to fit in the box. I'll start with . . . a pin.'

'A button,' suggested William.

And so they went on, until they had a complete list. It was six o'clock by the time they had found all the objects and packed them into the matchbox.

'Had a busy day, you two?' asked Dad.

William gave Dad the matchbox and watched as he opened it. 'Well,' said Dad, 'it certainly looks like fun.'

'It is,' replied William with another sneeze. 'Matchbox fun!'

Emily and the ducks

Emily opened her eyes, it was a beautiful morning. The sun was shining through the bedroom window and Pasha, her dog, was asleep at the side of her bed. Emily felt very happy. 'Time to get up Pasha,' she said, and sitting up on the bed she stretched her arms up as high as they would go. Pasha was up and waiting at the bedroom door. Emily put on her slippers and dressing gown, and together they made their way downstairs to the kitchen.

There was some ice-cold milk in the fridge and biscuits in the tin. Pasha was given a biscuit too which she crunched hungrily on the kitchen mat. When they had finished Emily went into the bathroom and put on her jeans and a cotton jumper. She went back into the kitchen and took a large loaf from the bread bin. Very carefully she cut a thick slice of bread and placing it in a paper bag put it into her pocket. Then she poured out a large bowl of milk and put it on the floor for the cats. Emily had three black cats. Their names were 'Bubbles', 'Squeak' and 'Pompi'. While they lapped happily at their milk Emily opened the kitchen door. 'Come on Pasha,' she said, 'let's go and feed the ducks.' They walked together down to the road and looking carefully both ways, crossed over to the meadow. Emily skipped along happily and Pasha ran round barking.

The ducks always seemed to know when someone was coming to feed them, and Emily could hear their loud welcome. 'Quack, quack, quack' they cried, 'quack, quack, quack'. As Emily stopped at the river bank they all came swimming over to where she was standing. Some of them were very tame and crept right up onto the bank so that they could catch any crumbs that might fall on the grass. Emily broke the bread into small pieces and threw them into the water. 'Splash, splash, quack, quack, quack'. Oh they were having a lovely time. When the bread was all gone Emily said goodbye to the ducks and she and Pasha started back for home.

When they came to the road they crossed carefully and made their way up to the little house. As they reached the gate Emily could see the three cats waiting to greet them. 'Here we are home again,' she said, 'and ready for a nice big breakfast.'

Jumping

I used to jump upon the couch
And then upon the chairs;
Once I jumped upon the bed
And all the way downstairs.
Now I'm well-behaved indoors,
For on the lawn so green
There's something made
*   to jump upon—*
A bouncy trampoline.

The Chinese garden

A grandfather clock stood in a shop looking down at the other furniture – two carved chairs, a polished table, a little oval mirror, and a glass-fronted bookcase. They had all been made many years ago. There were other old things for sale too – hand-painted plates, a brass kettle, jugs, teapots, silver spoons, and a little Chinese doll.

The grandfather clock was not for sale so he had seen many things come and go. The sad Chinese doll interested him. Her black hair was smooth, her feet small, and her satin dress narrow. The clock tried to cheer her up, but one day a red cabinet arrived and he was to change everything.

He was a painted cabinet on carved dragon's legs, with a Chinese garden painted on his doors.

That night the clock stopped, amazed to see these doors open and the doll go inside! Next morning, she was back in the shop window.

Every night she walked in the garden, under the willows beside the lake. But someone bought the cabinet. 'I am lost,' her eyes said to the clock, but he whispered across to her.

When the cabinet was collected next day nobody guessed she lay in his secret drawer. Now she walks in the Chinese garden whenever she wishes, and she is happy.

The goatherd and the troll

There once was a goatherd who took his flock to the pasture every morning. But he had been warned not to go over the mountain, for a big troll lived in the next valley.

One day the goatherd counted his flock and said, 'The little white goat with the twisted horns is missing. I must find her.'

He climbed higher and higher until he could see into the valley on the other side of the mountain. In the middle of a strange flock of goats was the little goat with the twisted horns.

Then the goathered could hear the crickets in the grass. They were saying, 'Run away, little goatherd, run far away, here comes the troll who eats a goat every day.'

When he saw the troll coming, the goatherd hid behind some rocks. The troll started to drive his flock down the mountainside but the white goat with the twisted horns led them away. The troll

Simon and Richard

I know two boys who look the same.
They're twins, you see, and it's a game
To tell one from his brother.
Now, Simon's nice, and lots of fun
But then, so is the other one —
They're copies of each other.
Sometimes I think they swap and
*   switch,*
Just so I don't know which is which.

I called young Simon by his name,
But RICHARD said: 'You're wrong
*   again.*
Say "RICHARD", and don't tease
*   me.'*
'Good morning, Richard,' I will say
When meeting him another day.
'Say "SIMON" – that will please me.'
Sometimes I think they swap and
*   switch,*
Just so I don't know which is which!

chased after her, but the little goat jumped from crag to crag. The troll tried to follow her, but he slipped and fell with a great splash into the river, far below.

The swiftly flowing river carried the troll far away and he was never seen again. But the clever little white goat came running back to the flock and the goatherd led them safely back over the mountain to his own pasture.

Claude gets stuck up the chimney

Claude was a cat that couldn't be good
He knew that he ought to
He knew that he should
He tried very hard
But try as he would
He was just a cat that couldn't be good.

Claude was a big, bold, black cat. He had white toes, a stripe on his nose. And he was BAD. He had always been bad. His mother used to say, 'Claude, why can't you behave?' But he couldn't. He was just a cat that couldn't be good.

When Claude was a kitten his mother taught his brother and sisters how to drink milk and wash their faces, but Claude went exploring instead. He thought soot would be much better for his coat than washing it. He felt sure that it would make him even blacker – even smarter – so he crept into the kitchen and over to the fireplace. He jumped up into the chimney where it was dark and full of dirt. He climbed and climbed until he was nice and sooty. And then he decided to come down again. But he couldn't! It was too hot. And the lower down the chimney he crept, the hotter he got . . . because someone had lit a fire in the fireplace. Now he was stuck, poor Claude!

Luckily, at that moment Mr Plum came into the kitchen carrying coal. Just as he bent down to throw it onto the fire he heard a 'mew' – and then a 'sneeze', and then a 'squeak!' He was very surprised. He quickly put out the fire.

When Claude's mother saw Mr Plum peering up the chimney and heard Claude's cries she soon guessed what had happened, 'Claude,' she said, 'come down from that chimney at once!'

'I can't,' cried Claude, 'I'm stuck.' Claude's mother swished her tail, waggled her whiskers, and sprang up the chimney but soon there were two cats stuck up the chimney instead of one.

Poor Mr Plum was most perplexed. He had to rescue both of the cats himself! He telephoned a friend who was a chimney sweep, and the man came with his big brush. Together they pushed it up the chimney and – SWOOSH! – it dislodged Claude's mother. She caught it with her back claws, and clutched Claude with her front paws, and together they tumbled down the chimney in a shower of soot. It covered the tables, the chairs, and even the clock.

'I thought soot was good for black cats,' said Claude.

'Well it isn't,' said his mother, 'and instead of getting yourself clean you have made everyone else dirty.' And then she softened and added, 'But I'm pleased to have you back.'

Old Man Glens

Old Man Glens
Had two hens
Which laid two eggs
Which hatched two chicks
Which grew two hens –
Now how many hens
Had Old Man Glens?

House wanted

Elfie the Elf lived in an acorn cup beneath an oak tree. One night there was a hail storm. Thunder growled. Lightning flashed. The oak tree fell. Elfie, in his acorn cup, rolled into a clover bed. The acorn cup was three-quarters full of water.

Elfie sighed and crawled out. He had to find a nice dry new home as soon as possible. Just then, Shelly Tortoise peered out of his shell.

'Hello, Shelly,' said Elfie. 'Have you heard of a house to let?'

'Who needs a house? Be like me and grow a shell,' said grumpy old Shelly.

Dan Dormouse peeped out of a hollow tree. 'Poor old Elfie', he said. 'Come in and get dry.'

Elfie had hot cocoa and toast and Danny told him that his cousin Daisy Dormouse had a spare house. The rent would be six snippets of corn and a piece of cheese a week.

Elfie was delighted. 'My friend Mr Farmer will give me the corn and Mrs Mary who keeps the dairy will give me the cheese,' he said.

So it was settled and Elfie moved into his nice new house. The address is: *Willow Nest, Willow Way, Greenwood*.

If ever you go walking that way, look out for him.

The clown's game

Tumble the Clown
Turns upside-down
With a smile, a shout
A wave, a frown.
On his head he often stands,
The children laugh and clap
      their hands.
His nose is red, his clothes are gay;
He thinks of many tricks to play.
He throws bright balls up in the air,
Can you find the matching pair?

The Bunnies' bedtime

Mrs Bunny was tired and Mr Bunny was yawning too, so they went to sleep in their big double bed.

In the other bedroom, Floppy slept in his little bed, and Loppy in his cot.

During the night, Loppy woke his Mummy. 'I had a nightmare,' he whimpered, and snuggled in beside her.

Then Floppy woke Mr Bunny. 'I heard thunder,' he said, and crept in beside him.

What a squeeze! Mrs Bunny couldn't sleep, so she got into Floppy's little bed, but her feet poked out of the end, and the covers were too short.

Next morning she was very stiff. She made the tea and took it to her bedroom. What a surprise! There, in the big bed, were Loppy and Floppy, sound asleep.

But where was Mr Bunny?

She searched the bedroom, the kitchen, even the bathroom. She peeped into her children's bedroom. There was Mr Bunny snoring his head off in Loppy's little cot. He did look funny with his two front paws poking out through the wooden bars.

'Oooh!' he cried when he woke up, 'I can't move.'

Bobbing balloons

Bobbing balloons,
Round as full moons!
There's brightest blue
For Sweety Sue
And cherry red
For chubby Fred.
There's emerald green
For shy Doreen
And Tommy is a lucky fellow —
His balloon is buttercup yellow!
There's one balloon left here for you —
Can you say its colour, too?

Giraffe's misadventure

Giraffe had gone mad. He had found some old pots of paint and was painting everything. He'd painted the toy cupboard doors, one red, one blue. He'd painted green spots on the little building bricks.

The toys asked him, begged him, even ordered him to stop, but he just ignored them.

'Ho, ho, ho, look at my beautiful table,' he boasted. The dolls' table was now orange with red spots and the chairs were red with purple stripes.

'I think I'll go for a walk,' sighed Edward Bear. 'Me too,' said Elephant. 'May I join you?' asked Rabbit. 'We'll all come,' said the dolls Wendy and Agatha.

Somehow Giraffe didn't find painting such fun with no-one to show off to. So he made himself a pot of tea and sat down.

When the others returned he offered them tea, but as he got up they all burst out laughing. 'Ho, ho, ho,' laughed Elephant. 'Ho, ho, ho,' laughed Edward Bear, 'look at your beautiful red-and-purple-striped bottom.'

The paint was still wet when Giraffe had sat down on the chair. They all roared with laughter. All, that is, except Giraffe.

208

A hard week's washing

Pip the pixie was very naughty. That morning he had flown into Mrs Moggs's garden, and pulled all the pegs from her washing-line. Now her clothes were lying in the mud. But he didn't know that Peterkin, the pixie chief was watching.

'I can't have this,' said Peterkin to himself. 'I must think of a way to punish him.'

So the next day, he called at Pip's cottage. 'I'm going to put a stop to your naughty tricks,' he said. 'You are coming with me.'

So off they went, until they came to the pixie's laundry.

'Now the pixies who work here, are going away for a week's holiday, and you are going to do their work all by yourself,' said Peterkin.

'All by myself?' echoed Pip.

'Yes, plenty of work will keep you out of mischief.'

And every day the pixies brought their laundry, and Pip washed, rinsed, starched and ironed, until his little arms ached.

But the clothes piled in, and he couldn't stop, until at last the pixies came back. He was very pleased to see them.

'Oh dear,' he said. 'I'm so tired, I never want to see a line of washing again.'

Sue's garden

One day, Mummy said she was going to do some gardening.

'May I do some too?' asked Sue. 'I'd like to grow some flowers all on my own in red and white and blue.'

'Yes, of course you can,' said Mummy.

At the gardening shop, Mummy bought some gardening gloves and seeds for herself, and a set of tiny garden tools for Sue, and her seeds for flowers – red and white and blue. Then they went back home and started their gardening.

Sue dug her small garden with her tiny trowel and forked the earth.

Mummy raked Sue's small garden until it was smooth and flat and then she told Sue to write her name in the soil with huge letters. Sue sowed her seeds into her name, and patted the earth down over them.

For a long time Sue watered and cared for her garden. Then one day, when the sun was shining, she looked out of the window and saw her name written in her small garden.

It said 'SUE' all in flowers of red and white and blue.

Sam the sailor doll

Sam was a sailor doll who longed to go to sea. He belonged to a boy called Billy.

One day Billy took Sam on holiday to the seaside. 'We are going for a trip round the bay,' Billy told him.

Off they went to the pier. First they saw some men fishing from the pier with long rods and lines. Then they went down some steps and onto a boat.

'This is exciting,' said Sailor Sam. Billy was leaning over the boat rail and Sam could see the water below him.

Suddenly the boat rocked and Billy let go of Sam. He fell, *splash*, into the water. 'Help, I can't swim!' he cried, but nobody seemed to hear him.

At last he felt something tugging at his collar. Up, up into the air he swung until *flop*, he landed on the pier. He had been caught on a fisherman's line.

'It's not a fish, it's a sailor doll,' the man said. 'I'd better throw it back into the sea.'

'Stop! That's Sam, my sailor doll.'

The boat had come back and Billy came running along the pier.

'Phew, that was a narrow escape!' gasped Sam. 'I don't mind if I never go to sea again.'

What is it?

Long and narrow
Lots of feet,
All you ever do is eat.
Pretty colours
Brown and green,
On leaves and hedges
You are seen.
In winter you will bundle up
Like a parcel all wrapped up.
And when the parcel comes undone . . .
A butterfly will greet the sun!

Duncan and Debbie the Dinosaurs

Alexander's amazing magnifying glass

Duncan and Debbie were bored. They had lived, for millions of years, in Brazil in a forest that no human had visited. They were the only dinosaurs left in the forest now.

'I'm lonely,' sighed Debbie.

All Duncan and Debbie had to do after their morning hunt for plants to eat was sit and look at each other. After millions of years of this, it isn't surprising that they were bored.

Then, one day, some explorers discovered the forest. At first they were terrified by the dinosaurs, but when they found out how friendly they were, the explorers were very excited. They rushed back through the forest and made their way to London, to tell everyone that they had found the only dinosaurs in the world.

Everyone wanted to see the dinosaurs, so special railways were built to carry people to the forest. Every day, people came, and the children loved to climb and slide on the dinosaurs' backs.

'Isn't it interesting, having all these visitors,' said Duncan. 'We're never bored or lonely now.'

'Stop talking, and smile nicely,' said Debbie. 'Here comes the next train-load of visitors.'

Alexander pressed his nose against the toyshop window and gazed at everything inside.

'I'd like the tractor, the scooter, the paddling pool and that furry panda,' he said for fun.

His mummy laughed. 'But you only have a little pocket money to spend! Come on, let's go inside,' she said.

Alexander took ages to decide, but in the end he bought a small round magnifying glass with the money he had saved.

It was just like magic peering through that magnifying glass. Everything seemed so huge! Currants in cakes looked like great black rocks and a drop of water like a puddle.

But one day Alexander couldn't find his magic glass. It certainly wasn't in his pocket. He searched for it high and low. Sadly he began to think it was lost forever.

Last of all he searched in his mummy's sewing basket. Alexander didn't notice straightaway but the magnifying glass was there all right.

But when he did see it he laughed and laughed for underneath was a blue button looking as big as a saucer with two holes in the middle. Well, almost as big anyway.

Painting the fence

Once there was a little boy called Michael. Round the garden of his house was a wooden fence. It used to be a white fence, but the rain had washed all the colour away.

One day, Michael's father said to him, 'I shall have to paint the fence a new colour. Would you like to help me?'

'Oh, yes please!' said the little boy.

But his father didn't paint it that day, nor the next day, nor the day after that. So Michael decided he would paint the fence all by himself, and give his father a surprise.

He didn't have any paint of his own, so instead, he mixed up some thick brown mud in his play bucket. Then he found his father's brush, and began to paint the mud all over the fence.

But oh dear, what a mess it made! And what a horrible colour!

When Michael's father came home from work and saw what he'd done, he began to laugh. 'Now I certainly shall have to paint the fence,' he said.

And Michael helped him. But this time he did it properly – with real paint.

The mouse in the mill

There once was a mouse who lived in a mill. But every time the miller saw the little mouse he chased him. Every time the miller's dog saw the little mouse he chased him. Every time the miller's cat saw the little mouse *she* chased him.

One day the miller was going to see a man about making some new sails for the mill. So he left the dog and cat to guard everything.

The dog and cat sat down outside the mill and they began to doze in the sun. Suddenly, the wind started blowing and it slammed the door, shutting the dog and cat outside. Then it began to rain and the dog and cat ran off to find shelter.

While they were gone, some robbers came along, opened the door of the mill and found all the miller's gold.

When the miller returned he was very angry. 'All my money has gone now, so I cannot buy any new sails. I will have to close the mill.'

So the dog and cat went off to work for the farmer. The miller shut the mill and the little mouse was left all on his own with no-one to chase him. He invited his best friends to come and live with him, and for all I know they may still be living there.

Sparkle

'Gosh, we're in fairyland,' said Mandy to her horse, Sparkle, as they trotted through a village full of mushroom houses.

Sparkle was a gift from the fairies, and Mandy had come to fairyland to find the Fairy Queen and thank her.

'Where does the Queen live?' Mandy asked a pixie who was working in his flower garden.

'Up there,' replied the pixie, pointing to a castle on the hill.

Mandy and Sparkle set off up the hill. It was a long way and it was growing dark by the time they reached the top. Mandy gasped, for there in front of them stood a

Riddle me

Riddle me one
I shine in the sun,
Riddle me two
My colour is blue,
Riddle me three
I run to the sea,
Riddle me four
I stop at the shore.
What am I?

real fairy castle covered with hundreds of brilliant fairy lights.

They were met at the gate by a group of fairies with flickering glow-worm torches and led inside to the Great Hall. There, on a throne of shining silver and velvet, sat the Fairy Queen.

'Happy birthday, Mandy dear.' Mummy and Daddy were smiling down at her, and the morning light was streaming in the window. By her bed stood her birthday present—a beautiful wooden rocking horse.

'I shall call him "Sparkle",' said Mandy, with a secret smile.

The woolly slippers

One day, Pam said to Peter, 'Let's ask Gran to teach us to knit. Then we can knit her some slippers and put budgerigars like her Sparky on them.

'You'll have to go round and find out how big Gran's feet are, first,' laughed Mum. 'Tell her to stand on some paper. Then draw round her feet and cut out the shapes they make.'

So Gran stood on some paper while Pam and Peter made the patterns. Gran was so pleased that she found some red wool and chubby knitting needles and showed them how to knit.

'How will we put budgerigars on them?' Peter asked Pam when they had finished knitting.

Pam smiled. She went to her toy box and guess what she found – two little yellow chickens from the top of their Easter eggs. 'One for each slipper,' she said. Pam and Peter carefully stuck the chicks on to the slippers, then took them round to Gran's.

When Gran's budgie Sparky saw her wearing the red slippers, he got quite excited and hopped about and tweeted.

'He likes them,' said Gran, 'And so do I!'

Memories

I remember, I remember
My first view of the dawn.
I'd gone camping with the Wolf Cubs
In the woods near Worplethorne.
I am not an early riser,
But there'd been a gale that night
And the wind had blown our tents down.
Just as it was getting light.

I remember, I remember
The day I saw the Queen.
The friendly wave she gave me
Was more than dull routine.
But of all my pleasant memories
There's one I shan't forget –
The Junior Gymkhana
When I won my first rosette!

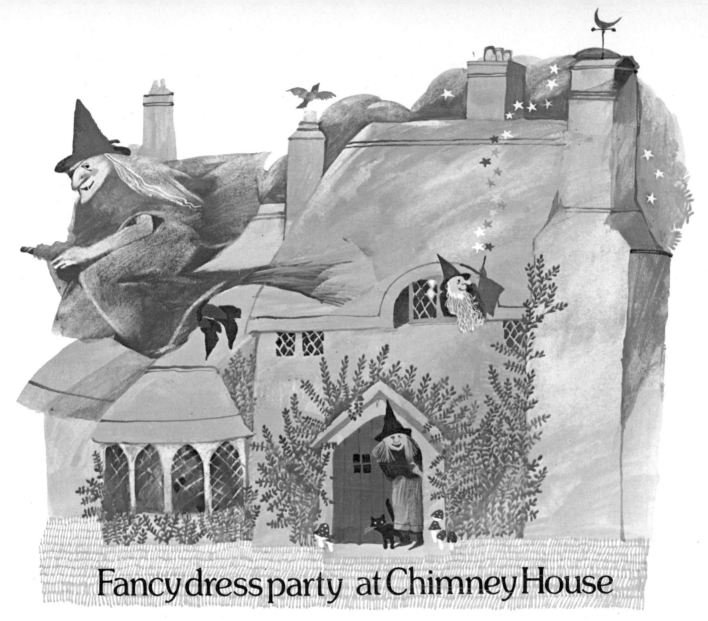

Fancy dress party at Chimney House

'Is this it?' Tommy asked his sister. He looked at the little house then at the invitation card he held.

'The card says *Fancy Dress Party at Chimney House*,' Tara answered. 'This house has lots of chimneys. There are people inside. This must be it.'

The two children – Tommy, dressed as a wizard, Tara as a witch – knocked on the door. A fat witch opened the door and smiled. 'Come in,' she said.

Tommy and Tara looked at each other in surprise. The house was full of wizards and witches. A wizard was waving his wand. Stars flew from it. He said a few words. The wand became a bird and flew up a chimney. Everyone clapped.

'Now do *your* magic,' the fat witch turned to Tommy.

'But I'm not a real wizard,' Tommy stuttered. 'We dressed this way for a party and . . .'

'They don't belong to us!' the wizards and witches cried.

There was a great puff of smoke. Wizards and witches vanished. The children stood in a field. Through the trees they saw a big house with chimneys.

'That's where the party is!' Tommy pointed.

'Won't we have lots to tell them,' Tara laughed.

John Dragon stops his dreaming

John Dragon so wanted to fly
That he stood on a hillside to try;
But his wings were too small,
And he couldn't at all
Leave the ground. He started to cry.

A bird said; 'My secret desire
Is to know how to breathe smoke
       and fire—
As you dragons can do,
So be glad you are you.
Don't dream about being a flier.'

The helpful bird then flew away,
And left John Dragon there to stay.
He stood and breathed fire-balls
       instead,
Then smiled and nodded his head—
'I'm glad I'm a dragon,' he said.
       'Hooray!'

The trouble with icecream

Jennifer wished grown-ups didn't talk so much. She wanted to get home for lunch, and eat the icecream her mother had just bought, and put in her plastic carrier-bag.

But her mother stood talking to Mrs Marsh, the shopkeeper, about the hot weather, and the price of meat, and how sweet the Harrisons' new kitten was.

At last, they walked home. But outside, they met Mrs Dibbs, who stopped for a chat with Jennifer's mother. They talked about the hot weather, and the price of meat, and how sweet the Harrisons' new kitten was . . .

Jennifer thought about the icecream, and looked into the bag. In the bottom, sloshing around, was a big white pool—the icecream had all melted!

'Mum, look!' said Jennifer.

'Oh, dear!' cried her mother.

Jennifer felt like crying, but when they went in, her mother said, 'Never mind—I've got an idea.'

She carefully poured the melted icecream into a jug. Then she cut two pieces of apple pie and gave one to Jennifer in a bowl.

'There you are,' she said. 'Just pour the icecream over the pie. It's my new invention—apple pie with icecream sauce. It will taste delicious.' And it did.

Sammy Rabbit and the cake

Sammy Rabbit was always in trouble. Even when it wasn't his fault he got the blame.

One day, the Rabbit children were very excited. Mrs Rabbit had baked a lovely cake with icing and candles for Rosie Rabbit's birthday.

'Now Rabbits,' she said, 'get ready, and don't forget to brush your tails.'

They all scampered away and washed their faces and brushed their tails and combed their whiskers, and when they were quite ready they tumbled quickly downstairs.

The table was laid with lovely things to eat. But there was something missing – *the cake had gone*!

'OOOOH,' squealed all the rabbits at once.

'Sammy's taken it,' shouted Bobby Rabbit.

'He's eaten it,' cried Rosie.

Poor Sammy. They made such a din that he rushed outside and hid in a rhubarb patch.

Mrs Rabbit came in to see what all the fuss was about.

'Sammy's eaten the cake,' they wailed.

'You silly Rabbits,' said Mrs Rabbit. 'I put the cake in the larder to keep it fresh.'

When they had found Sammy and wiped away his tears, they sat down to the best party they'd ever had.

And guess who had the biggest piece of cake!

The patient Prince of Pumperdinkum

The Patient Prince of Pumperdinkum ruled his land with patience. He waited for his peasants to harvest the crops. He waited for his army to guard the castle. He waited for carpenters to repair the drawbridge and engineers to fill the moat.

And his people? Well, they did very little work and laughed at their Patient Prince.

One day, while he was waiting, the Prince wrote a letter, posted it and then waited patiently.

Soon a great army appeared outside the castle. Everyone could tell it was King Ernest the Energetic's by its red flag. His army took the crops. They crossed the dry moat, marched over the broken drawbridge and into the castle.

'Ernest, you have come. My castle is yours,' the Prince said. 'It's no good being patient. Just leave me one room where I can read in peace.'

Now King Ernest the Energetic rules all Pumperdinkum. Orders are given. Things get done at once.

And the people?

Secretly they dream of the easy-going days of the Patient Prince and wish they had worked harder for him.

Ducklings in a line

Seven little ducklings walking in a line,
Up come another two, and that makes
    nine.
One sees a thistle-down and chases it
    away
And two more decide to stay behind and
    play.
Then three little ducklings are
    frightened by a cow,
So how many ducklings are left in line
    now?

Fred the floating football

Tommy had a football, which he called 'Fred'. One day, Fred lay in the garden, looking at the sky.

'I wonder what it's like, up there?' he thought.

Tommy came, and threw Fred into the air – but he didn't come down. He floated up, up, up, through the clouds and into the sunshine.

Tommy's mother said, 'It can't have disappeared. It's probably in the bushes. We'll find it later.'

But that didn't make Tommy feel any better.

When it got dark, people on Earth looked up through telescopes, and were very excited. They said:

'It's a new star!'

'It's a satellite!'

'It's a flying saucer!'

But Tommy said, 'It's my football.'

Everyone laughed, but Tommy knew he was right.

Fred began to feel lonely and cold in the dark sky, and when morning came, he floated down, down, into the garden again.

Tommy's mother saw him lying there, and said, 'Look, the football was there all the time!'

Tommy ran out and picked Fred up. 'Hello, Fred,' he said. And he was sure that Fred smiled . . .

The King
who couldn't laugh

King Bindweed was rather a miserable King. Just now he was having a grumble about the weather. It had been raining for days, and even Queen Hollyhock couldn't make him smile.

'Please come out and cheer up the King,' she said to the sun, who proudly obeyed.

The King took the Queen to the sunny seaside, but that didn't make him very happy. A crab bit his toe, his bucket and spade floated out to sea, and a little boy buried his crown in the sand.

So the rain and the sun thought of what they could do together to make King Bindweed smile again.

The sun shone exactly the same moment as the rain poured down, and a beautiful rainbow appeared, arching right over the palace.

'Lovely!' cried Queen Hollyhock, clapping her hands.

The King was pleased and began to smile. Then the Queen found two umbrellas and took King Bindweed for a walk round the palace garden and alongside a lake.

The King said, 'Whoever is that miserable old man staring at me out of the lake?'

'You, my dear,' replied Queen Hollyhock. 'That is your reflection!'

When King Bindweed saw how miserable he really looked, he couldn't stop laughing!

Peter and the painter

Peter and his puppy were playing in the garden while the painter was working. He had just finished painting the front of the house yellow with a smart white fence.

'Nice surprise for Mum when she comes home from the shops,' said the painter proudly.

Peter threw his big red ball in the air and the puppy got very excited. Peter was chasing after him when he saw the painter coming round into the back garden carrying a large pot of yellow paint.

'Look out!' cried Peter, but he tripped over the puppy under his feet. They both collided with the painter who fell headlong on the grass.

Yellow paint spilled everywhere and the puppy ran about in it, barking happily.

Daddy came outside. He helped the poor surprised painter to his feet and gathered up what was left of the tin of yellow paint.

Nobody saw the puppy, running and jumping after the painter as he went round to the front garden to fetch another tin of paint.

But when Mummy came home from the shops she stared in amazement. The front path and the new white fence were covered in very yellow, very wet, very doggy footprints!

Message in a bottle

I bought some lemonade,
And I sat down in the shade
To sip its bubbling coolness through a
*   straw.*
And I wrote a friendly note
To put in my glassy boat,
For I didn't need the bottle any more.

I dropped it in the stream,
(How brightly did it gleam!)
As the current took it far, far out of
*   sight.*
It now must be at sea,
Where the waves are salt and free,
And the seagulls swoop on wings of
*   startling white.*

May it find some desert isle,
And bring a hopeful smile
To shipwrecked sailors waiting day
*   and night.*

Hickory, Dickory and Dock

There were once three mice – Hickory, Dickory and baby Dock – and they went to live inside a tall old clock. They had to keep very quiet, though, because down by the fire a big cat lay sleeping.

But when the clock began to chime – dong! dong! dong! – the noise frightened baby Dock and made him cry.

The cat woke up at once. 'Miaow,' it said, 'I hear a mouse.'

What were the mice to do? Each time the clock chimed, Dock would cry, and the cat would come to hunt them.

Hickory ran up the tall clock. 'Please, Clock,' he said, 'your loud chimes frighten baby Dock, so do you think you could be quiet?'

'Tick-tock,' said the clock. 'But if I do not chime, I can't tell the time. Tick-tock, tick-tock. Tell Dock I will strike no more than one chime.'

So on the hour the clock only ever struck one, and baby Dock stayed asleep. And so did the cat by the fire.

The dream

How nice it would be
To go down to the sea
And build a castle of sand.
I'd walk along the old iron pier
And listen to the band.

I'd paddle in the salty pools
Or form a cricket team,
And then, when I was quite worn out
I'd eat a HUGE ice-cream.

The first long dress

Joanna was three and a half years old, and she had been invited to a birthday party.

'I think that Joanna is old enough now to have a long dress,' said Mum.

'She would only trip over it, and tear it,' said Joanna's brother, Dominic, who was nearly six.

The next time Mum went shopping, she saw a long dress with a pretty flowery pattern, and it was just Joanna's size. She liked it so much that she bought it, and took it home. Joanna was delighted, and she wore it to her party on Saturday. She had a lovely time, and everyone said her first long dress looked very nice indeed.

'Did you trip over it?' asked Dominic, when he and Mum collected her after the party.

'Only once,' declared Joanna. 'But I didn't tear it. And I've been asked to another party – in two weeks' time.'

Mum and Dominic smiled.

'I think our little girl has become quite a grown-up lady!' said Mum.

The doll and the pram

Jane had a doll called Elizabeth, and a little pram to push her about in. Elizabeth secretly wanted to get out of the pram and push it herself, so one night when Jane was asleep, she climbed out and whispered to Tom Teddy Bear: 'Tom, get into the pram.'

She was rather a bossy doll, so Tom did as he was told.

Elizabeth found the pram was heavier than she thought, and she couldn't move it. So she stepped back and took a run at it. This time the pram moved very fast, with Tom inside and Elizabeth clinging to the handle.

The pram went whizzing out of Jane's door, on to the landing, and *bump-bump-bump-bump* down the stairs.

'*Crash!*' It landed at the bottom and tipped over, throwing Tom out on top of Elizabeth.

Jane's mother came into the hall and saw them. She thought Jane had thrown all her toys downstairs. But when she carried them upstairs, Jane was still fast asleep.

'That's odd,' said her mother. 'Sometimes I think these toys have a life of their own.'

Tom winked at Elizabeth, and Elizabeth winked back. But she never tried pushing the pram again.

Percy's sunflowers

Percy, Jonathan's tame parrot, liked to boast about his bright and beautiful colours.

'Pretty Percy!' he shouted, swinging on his perch in the front garden where everyone could see and admire him.

One day he opened his big curved beak and squawked so loudly that he dropped the sunflower seeds that Jonathan had given him to eat. They fell into the flower bed.

After a while the sunflowers began to grow. They grew taller and taller, until one day there was a row of huge yellow sunflower faces for people to see.

Everyone who walked by stopped to look at the beautiful sunflowers. Percy felt sad because he wanted people to like him best. While Jonathan wasn't looking, he flew up into a tree and sulked in the branches. Then he heard children laughing and he saw that they were laughing at Jonathan, who was hiding behind the sunflowers and peeping out at his friends.

Jonathan looked so funny that Percy, who loved to copy noises, laughed too.

'Clever Percy,' cried Jonathan. Percy flew down and sat on Jonathan's shoulder. All the children came to see the lovely coloured parrot who could talk and laugh.

'Clever Percy!' croaked Percy.

Cowboy

When I'm Buffalo Bill or Lone Ranger,
I'm tough, law-abiding but just
And my greatest delight
Is a gun-slinging fight,
With my enemies biting the dust.

I don't care if it's one of the James boys
Or the Sherriff of Fractured Jaw.
When I reach for my gun,
They all turn and run,
Because I'm so quick on the draw.

But whenever the posse surrounds me,
I still go on playing it cool;
And on the point of arrest
I just leave the Wild West
And change back to a small boy at school!

Granny goes shopping

Timothy's Granny was called Granny Muddles. She didn't look like a witch but she did strange little tricks from time to time.

One day, Mummy asked Timothy to go shopping for her. Timothy said he would if Granny Muddles could go with him.

Inside the supermarket a customer was piling all her shopping into a wire trolley. There was a gingerbread man on top.

'I wish my basket was bigger,' the woman said.

At once, Granny Muddles pointed her little magic silver pencil at the basket but by mistake it tapped the gingerbread man on the nose.

He grew bigger and bigger and climbed out of the trolley, to the delight of all the customers. He did a little dance and then started to sing in a deep, gingery voice.

So many shoes!

Jennifer Jane has so many shoes,
She can never decide which pair to
*   choose.*
There are two yellow slippers, and two
*   with red bows,*
And two that are sandals to show off
*   her toes,*
And two that are wellington boots for
*   the rain.*
So how many shoes has Jennifer Jane?

'This is fun!' cried Timothy.

But unfortunately Granny couldn't remember how to stop the magic. The giant gingerbread man knocked over tins and boxes as he walked about. Apples and sweets rolled everywhere. Then he marched through the open doorway, eating a lollipop. He jumped on a bus, and was never seen again.

'You're a super Granny,' said Timothy. 'I think I like shopping now.'

Home is the best place

Joey the tortoise was very happy. Someone had left the garden gate open, and now he could wander where he liked.

'Where are you going Joey?' asked Lucy the kitten.

'First, I'd like to find the field where the strawberries grow. You wouldn't know where that is I suppose?'

'No I don't like strawberries myself. Sorry!' And off she went.

When Joey reached the main road he was rather frightened. 'Why is everything going so fast?' he said. He trotted halfway across the road and then stopped. Poor Joey! A terrified little tortoise was trapped between two lines of cars. But a van stopped, and he was gently picked up and put inside.

In the meantime, Jenny had found that Joey had gone and she was very upset. She and her mummy spent nearly all day looking for him.

Early the next morning the doorbell rang.

It was Jimmy the milkman.

'Good morning, Jenny,' he said. 'Here you are, two pints of milk and one tortoise.'

'Oh Mummy,' cried Jenny. 'Joey's back, Jimmy's found him.'

When Joey heard Jenny's voice, he opened his sleepy eyes. 'So I'm home again,' he thought. 'It's the best place after all.'

227

Claude goes canoeing

The kittens loved spring, for their mother allowed them to play in the garden every day and they made lots of new friends.

One of them was Tabby Tim who came of a sea-faring strain of cats. His ancestors had sailed with Captain Cook, and Tabby Tim could tell remarkable tales. The kittens loved to listen to his sea-stories. He told them about gales and galleons, and sailors and storms, and parrots and pieces of eight. Claude wished that he could have been a ship's cat too.

One morning the kittens went to visit Boffin Bark. He was busy burying bones, so they decided to play hide and seek. Claude found a secret hiding-place under a heavy canvas sheet. He settled

down and was soon asleep dreaming of sailing. The sea swayed, waves wet his whiskers, and the water tickled his toes. At that moment he awoke. He discovered that he really was wet – water was slopping over the side of his hiding-place which seemed to be speeding along! The sheet that had covered the craft had gone, and now he could see the sky! What was happening? Claude quickly climbed to look over the side, and there he saw white water and silver spray. The curious craft was a canoe and it was rushing down a rough river! On and on it sped over the tossing water and Claude felt a little afraid. But soon the river was smooth and still again, and the canoe slowed down and stopped. Thomas, Boffin Bark's owner, stepped out of the canoe. He hadn't seen Claude concealed in the canoe when he had set out for the river.

All the other kittens listened to Claude's sailing story with envy. Now he was a real ship's cat!

Fiona
and the fairy

Fiona came creeping downstairs one starry Christmas Eve to peep at the Christmas tree.

'I wish you were real,' she said to the pretty fairy on top of the tree.

'Of course I'm real,' replied the fairy.

At once Fiona could see she was in fact a very bad fairy with bright beady eyes, looking for mischief.

Fiona watched in astonishment as the fairy went flying round the Christmas tree and did all sorts of naughty things.

She swung on the little parcels, pulled faces at herself in the baubles, turned the tree lights on and off and lit the tiny candles with her wand.

'You're a very rude and horrid fairy,' said Fiona. 'And I wish you'd go away.'

Then the door opened, and in came Father Christmas. He tried to catch the fairy, but Fiona's cat crept in through the open door and chased after her. The fairy vanished down a mouse hole, trailing a piece of tinsel behind her.

Then Father Christmas put a beautiful star on top of the Christmas tree. 'Straight from the sky,' he smiled.

On Stage

When my class at school
Puts on a play,
As a general rule
I keep well away.
In the parts I'm allowed
There's little to do,
Such as 'Boy in the Crowd',
Or 'One of the Crew',
Or 'Elderly Waiter',
Or 'Second Page',
Or just 'Spectator',
Or 'Voice Off-stage'.
I know I'm not clever,
But joking apart,
Why can't I ever
Play the main part?

229

Lucy Bodkin makes things better

Lucy Bodkin was a happy little lady. Lorna her pet goat was a happy little goat. But Bizzy-Lizzy on the windowsill was not happy at all. Her pretty pink blossoms drooped and huge teardrops splashed down from her shiny green leaves.

'Poor Bizzy-Lizzy,' said Lucy Bodkin. 'Perhaps you are a Lonely-Lizzy. I'll find you a friend, that's what I'll do.'

All at once she had a good idea! She planted a fat purple bean in a jam jar and watered it and cared for it every day. Before long that fat purple bean grew some hairy roots. Then one day, at the top of the jam jar, up popped two leaves on a stalk.

'Hello,' said the plant in its peculiar beany voice. 'My name is Runner-Bean.'

Well, Runner-Bean turned out to be the friendliest plant you could imagine. With big heart shaped leaves it grew and climbed all around the window frame. Of course Bizzy-Lizzy was there too, happy again and covered in new pink blossoms. Together they filled up the whole window.

Lucy Bodkin didn't mind at all. She was very pleased that Bizzy-Lizzy was happy again.

The Sandman's shoes

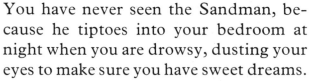

You have never seen the Sandman, because he tiptoes into your bedroom at night when you are drowsy, dusting your eyes to make sure you have sweet dreams.

But, one night, the Sandman was very worried. You see, he had a new pair of shoes. The leather was hard and stiff and the shoes squeaked.

'SQUEAK! S-Q-U-E-A-K!'

'This is terrible,' gasped the Sandman. 'I can't wear shoes that squeak like this. The noise will wake the children.'

Now, the Sandman had three little elves to look after him. Their names were Snoozum, Snorum, and Sleepyboots.

They thought very hard, and they had an idea. They took the shoes into their tiny kitchen, and they rubbed best butter all over the leather. Soon, the soles of the shoes were quite soft.

Then, the elves fitted them on the Sandman's feet. He stood up, and you could hear a pin drop as he walked across the room. He was as quiet as a mouse in his shoes.

Off went the Sandman to visit all the children and wish them a good night's sleep. And I expect he called at your house, too!

Sir Wouldwin's horse

A knight wanting to do brave deeds must have a horse to match. But Sir Would win's horse hated court tournaments, and the word 'battle' made his knees tremble.

So Sir Wouldwin sadly decided to ride off into the forest. At nightfall they reached a castle and Sir Wouldwin put his horse in the stable and went to bed.

His horse found a friend in the stable and with noses together, they spent the night snorting and whickering.

Before sunrise Sir Wouldwin saddled up. His horse seemed refreshed, his ears pricked. Soon he was dancing and tossing his head. 'Amazing!' said Sir Wouldwin.

They sped through the forest, Sir Wouldwin laughing with joy. After a week they had rescued three fair maidens, and defeated four wicked knights.

Travelling home, they passed the castle. 'I've no regrets,' neighed a horse pulling a plough nearby.

'Nor I,' replied the knight's horse.

I expect you have guessed now that Sir Wouldwin had saddled the wrong horse in the dark, and the horses had made sure that he did!

Day and night birds

When I can hear the farm cock crow
It's time to get up, that I know,
But when the owl hoots loud and clear
Then I am sure that bedtime's near.

The lark is wide-awake at dawn
When I can only stretch and yawn,
But when the night a bright moon
*   brings,*
The nightingale so sweetly sings.

The new wellingtons

It was raining hard. Jonathan looked out of the window with his mummy. They were waiting to go to the shops.

'It's no good, Jonathan, we shall have to go in spite of the rain,' said his mummy, so she went to the hall cupboard and got out their raincoats and umbrellas and wellington boots.

Jonathan was really beginning to look forward to splashing his way through the puddles and wearing his sou'wester.

They were almost ready. Mummy just had to put on his wellingtons but – oh dear, they didn't fit him any more. Mummy pushed and so did Jonathan, but his wellingtons refused to go on.

'It doesn't matter, Mummy,' said Jonathan. 'Look – the rain is going to stop soon.'

The sun shone through and so off they went to the shops.

'The first thing on my list is to buy a new pair of wellington boots for you, Jonathan,' said his mummy.

They went into the shoe shop and Jonathan couldn't resist the bright, shiny yellow wellingtons that matched his raincoat and sou'wester.

He kept them on and after Mummy had finished the rest of her shopping they started to walk home.

New black clouds gathered overhead, and soon it was pouring with rain again. Well, do you know, Jonathan James and his mummy didn't mind at all! Mummy put up her umbrella and Jonathan James had a wonderful time splashing in and out of the puddles.

The Swallows' nest

One day Swoopy Swallow and his wife flew into Farmer Brown's big barn. 'Here's our old nest,' said Mrs Swoopy. 'But oh dear, it *does* need mending.'

'How shall we mend it?' asked Swoopy.

'We need some mud and some straw,' Mrs Swoopy told him.

'There's mud in the duck pond and straw in the stable,' said Swoopy.

So they flew to the duck pond first and filled their beaks with mud. Then they flew to the stable and filled their beaks with straw.

They worked very hard, mending the nest until it was as good as new. 'We've made a good job of that,' said Swoopy.

'It's not very soft inside,' Mrs Swoopy told him. 'We need some warm feathers to line it.'

Now, feathers were harder to find, but at that very moment Mrs Brown, the farmer's wife, was shaking a feather pillow in her bedroom. She was just plumping it up well when one of the seams split and the pillow burst open.

The feathers went flying all over the room. A lot of them floated out of the open window and Swoopy caught them in his beak.

Mrs Brown was cross about the mess the feathers had made, but Mrs Swoopy was very pleased to have the soft, warm feathers to line her nest.

The spider

The spider spun a silky web
Right above Amanda's bed.
When she awoke and said, 'Oh, no,
I'm sorry, but you'll have to go,'
The spider said, 'Don't be surprised.
I'm not going to harm you, I only eat flies.'

'In that case, I don't mind at all,'
Amanda sweetly said.
'And now I'll ask my mummy
Not to sweep you off the wall
Above my little bed.'

Bobby and Spud the bin men

'We're going to the doctor's today,' said Pam and Peter's Mum.

The doctor's surgery was in the shopping centre. But when they got there it was so early that the shops were still closed with boxes and sacks stacked outside.

'It's bin day,' said Pam.

'And there's the dust-bin tipper lorry,' said Peter. 'The one Bobby and Spud drive. Look, Bobby's waving to us!'

'Spud's gone to the doctor's,' said Bobby. 'He cut his finger.'

'We'd better help Spud when he comes to empty our bin at home,' said

Peter. 'Let's give him something nice for his tipper – like Dad's old car tyres.'

'But Dad might need them,' said Pam.

When Spud saw the tyres, he said, 'Sorry son, too big for us. Ask your Dad to ring the cleansing department.'

'Thank goodness!' said Pam.

Then Spud said, 'But I've got something for you today. Number 14 gave it to me.' And he climbed into the cab and brought out a red plastic boat.

'You lucky thing,' said Pam.

'Let's go and sail it in the park,' said Peter.

And they did. The park had a nice shallow paddling pool which was just right for sailing boats.

Two mice and a rocking chair

Cedric Mouse lived in the wall of the topmost flat in the block. The people who lived there were rich and he grew fat on cake crumbs.

'If I had a rocking-chair like Fred Mouse, I would be really happy,' he sighed.

Fred Mouse lived at the bottom of the

Down in the jungle

One hippopotamus opening his jaws,
Two hungry crocodiles sharpening
their claws,
Three puffing elephants cooling in the
breeze,
Four long-necked giraffes nibbling at
the trees,
Five stripey zebras galloping around,
Six snakes slithering and sliding on the
ground,
Seven pink flamingoes splashing in the
pool,
Eight merry monkeys playing April
Fool,
Nine pretty parakeets preening in the
sun,
Ten little lions asleep when day is done.

flats. Cedric decided to visit him. He pitter-pattered down five lots of stairs and was quite puffed out.

'Good evening, Fred,' he panted. 'That's a very nice chair you have.'

'You can have it in exchange for your nice home,' said Fred who was unhappy in his damp cellar. 'You wouldn't have to carry it up the stairs if you lived here,' he added.

Cedric Mouse agreed. The rocking-chair was very comfortable indeed. However, he soon tired of stale crusts and longed for his old home.

One day Fred came to visit.

'I'm so lonely in the top flat,' he said. 'Would you like to come back and share it with me?'

'Yes please,' said Cedric.

They picked up the rocking-chair and climbed the stairs, and when they got to the top they feasted on cake to celebrate.

Corky's ride home

Corky Piglet was waiting for his Mamma outside the greengrocer's in Piggytown, when he saw Mr Hubble-Bubble, the balloon man.

'Ah, Corky! How about minding my balloons while I pop in here for some lunch?' said Mr Hubble-Bubble, handing them over.

But no sooner had he gone into the sandwich shop, than – WOOOSH – up into the air went the balloons with Corky clinging to the strings.

Just then, Mamma Pig came out of the greengrocer's – no Corky! Mr Hubble-Bubble came out of the sandwich shop – no Corky, no balloons!

'Come with me,' said Mamma Pig, 'and we'll see if Corky's taken the balloons home with him.'

As they turned in the garden gate, they both gasped with fright – for there, caught up high in a tree was a bunch of balloons with Corky dangling below.

'Well, that was a quick ride home,' grinned Corky when he had been rescued.

And they all laughed and, carrying the bunch of balloons between them, they went inside for tea.

Wizard Whirlabout's invention

'My invention will shake the world,' cried Wizard Whirlabout, as he flew from one side of his laboratory to the other. Milton the magician sat listening. He was the Wizard's best friend.

'People will gasp when they see my work, Milton. They will all say what a clever Wizard Whirlabout I am.'

'Am I the first to see this marvellous invention?' asked Milton quietly.

'Why, yes, of course,' boomed the Wizard. 'You're my best friend, aren't you? Now are you ready?' And throwing back a curtain, he announced, 'Here it is, after months of planning and building – A GO-KART!'

And with a flick of his wrist, the Wizard threw off his pointed hat and long gown. There stood plain Johnny Jones in jeans and a jumper!

'Come on Dave, take off that silly cloak and we'll go and try it out on the hills.'

'Well, it may not shake the world,' said Dave as they wheeled the go-kart out of the shed, 'but it will certainly surprise the other children.'

The magic seashell

Janet was playing on the beach when she saw a big, pointed shell. It looked like a trumpet so she tried to blow through it.

There was a sound like the wind and suddenly a big wave rolled up with a shell boat on it. Inside was a mermaid. 'Jump in,' said the mermaid. 'I will take you to Father Neptune.'

Janet got into the boat and the wave took it far out to sea. Soon she could see an island with bright yellow sands and a large palace made of white shells.

The shell boat rocked gently to the shore and as Janet climbed out, Father Neptune himself came out of the palace.

'Welcome, little landmaid,' he said to Janet. 'I have brought you here to grant you a wish. You can have anything you like, so long as it comes out of the sea.'

'Ask for a coral necklace,' whispered the mermaid. 'That will bring good luck.'

'A coral necklace, please,' said Janet, and King Neptune clapped his hands.

Another mermaid came out of the palace with a necklace. She put it round Janet's neck and the next moment Janet found herself back on the beach. She was still wearing the coral necklace, so she knew she hadn't dreamt it all.

Bedtime

*B is for the cosy Bed I'm tucked in
every night,
E is for the Evening when the sun puts
out its light,
D is for the Dog in his basket on the
floor,
T is for the Toys asleep behind their
cupboard door,
I is for the Icecream that I had today
for tea,
M is for the Moon that shines when
no-one's there to see,
E is for the End of bedtime tales for
you and me.*